BRITISH MEN OF SCIENCE

General Editor
Sir Gavin de Beer F.R.S. F.S.A.
membre correspondant de l'Institut de France

Charles Lyell

CHARLES LYELL

Sir Edward Bailey F.R.S.

Doubleday & Company, Inc.
Garden City, New York
1963

Contents

v

List of Plates

List of Figures

Acknowledgments

The author wishes to acknowledge the kindness of the following
in supplying and giving permission for the use of illustrations:
The Board of Trustees of the National Galleries of Scotland
(Pl. 1); the British Museum (Natural History) (Pl. 23); the
Controller of H.M. Stationery Office (Pls. 5 and 21); S. Dodgson
Esq (Pl. 3); Ewing Galloway, N.Y. (Pl. 18); the Geological
Society of London (Pl. 24); John Leng & Co Ltd (Pl. 12); The
Rt. Hon. Lord Lyell (Pl. 2); Macmillan & Co Ltd (Figs. 2, 4,
and 12); Paul Popper Ltd (Pl. 4); Presidenza del Consiglio dei
Ministri, Rome (Pl. 19); Scotsman Publications Ltd (Pl. 15);
United States Information Service (Pl.14).

Plate 5 is from *British Regional Geology, the Wealden District*;
Plate 21 is Crown copyright.

Geological Time-table

The following time-table is offered for reference purposes to non-geological readers of this particular book. Thanks to changes that have occurred during past ages in the plant and animal populations of the world, geologists have been able to establish a time-scale covering events that are recorded in the rocks. Names on this basis have been introduced for a host of time-divisions, some relatively small, others much larger. These divisions do not have the regularity of years, months, days, etc., so that their nomenclature becomes very complex, though the principles involved are quite simple. For instance, Lias time is later than Trias time, and earlier than Oolite time; while Lias and Oolite times together constitute Jurassic time, which in turn occupies a mid position in Mesozoic time. Many sub-divisions of Lias time have been named, but we are not concerned with them here.

CAINOZOIC

QUATERNARY (Age of Man)
Recent or *Post-Glacial*, continuing today
Glacial or *Pleistocene*

TERTIARY (Age of pre-human Mammals)
Pliocene (regarding *Crag* in East Anglia see p. 127)
Miocene
Oligocene
Eocene
Paleocene

MESOZOIC or SECONDARY (Age of Reptiles and Ammonites)
Cretaceous
Chalk
Greensands and Gault
Wealden

Jurassic
Oolite
Lias

Trias, often grouped with Permian as *New Red Sandstone*

PALAEOZOIC
Permian
Magnesian Limestone or Zechstein
Rothliegendes

Carboniferous (Age of Amphibia)
Coal Measures
Millstone Grit
Carboniferous Limestone

Devonian including *Old Red Sandstone* (Age of Fishes)

Silurian
Ordovician } (Age of Trilobites and Brachiopods)
Cambrian

PRECAMBRIAN (Age of unrecorded life and earlier)

Chapter 1

1797-1815

Boyhood

1797-1810 Early Boyhood

Charles Lyell was born on 14 November 1797. This was a truly memorable year: in it Napoleon isolated Britain by forcing surrender on Naples and Austria; in it our sailors mutinied at Spithead and the Nore; in it also, as geologists recall, James Hutton of Edinburgh died. The perils of war were eventually surmounted by the victories of Nelson and Wellington. It still remained for the infant of 1797 to gain general acceptance for the most fundamental and perhaps most unpopular of Hutton's highly controversial teachings. This was no less than the doctrine now known in English by the uncouth title *uniformitarianism*, in French *actualisme*. Its gist is that processes that have been actually observed to modify the face of the earth during historic times may be taken as a safe and sufficient guide in interpreting the record of events dating from the long ages of the geological past. Most students of earth history in Lyell's early days opposed this doctrine. They were *Catastrophists* who, for instance, attributed the main features of scenery to sudden upheavals, accompanied by transient torrents. The recurrent disasters which they invoked were of a scope and intensity never witnessed by man since the days of Noah.

Charles was born at Kinnordy, the family estate, six miles northwest of Forfar, capital of the County of Angus (Forfarshire). The photograph of the house reproduced

1

in Plate 2 very definitely suggests both affluence and influence. Fortunately, father Charles Lyell, a thirty year old Cambridge graduate, combined these two attributes with a love of natural history and of Italian literature. He had made definite contributions to botany, especially in relation to the cryptogams or seedless plants, among which he had found certain new species. From botany he had turned to entomology, which, however, he soon abandoned, owing, it appears, to a distaste for killing insects. Study of Dante followed, leading to the publication of several commentaries and translations. As we follow his son through boyhood and maturity we shall find in him a naturalist by virtue of heredity and opportunity, one moreover who drew much geological knowledge from Italian exposures and Italian writings, and who was himself an eager and successful author. After saying all this one must admit that there is no evidence of father Lyell having given personal encouragement in the early stages of his son's naturalistic activities, perhaps because these started with entomology; but, as we shall presently see, his library did help very considerably.

Charles's mother was a daughter of Thomas Smith of Maker Hall, Swaledale, Yorkshire. He was thus by parentage half Scots, half English. On the other hand, his birth in Scotland was more than countered by his upbringing mainly in Hampshire, Wiltshire, Sussex, Oxford, and East Anglia; so that he felt the South to be his home, rather than the North (Fig. 1).

Charles was destined to be an indefatigable traveller throughout his life, and he started his journeyings, involuntarily, when only three months old. On this occasion he accompanied his parents on a leisurely tour, calling in turn at Inveraray, Ilfracombe, Weymouth, and Southampton. Here brother Tom put in an appearance. Brother Henry and seven sisters were to follow.

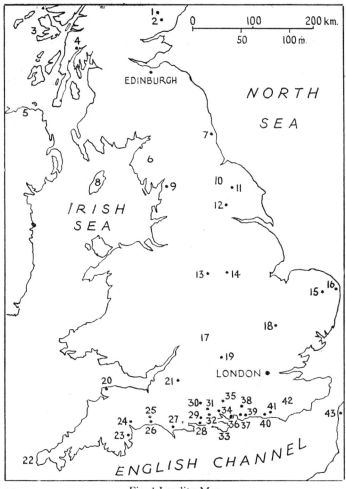

Fig. 1 Locality Map

1. Kinnordy	11. Kirkdale Cavern	22. Land's End	33. Isle of Wight
2. Forfar	12. York	23. Torquay	34. Southampton
3. Staffa	13. Derby	24. Exeter	35. Winchester
4. Inveraray	14. Nottingham	25. Axminster	36. Portsmouth
5. Giant's Causeway	15. Norwich	26. Lyme Regis	37. Chichester
6. Lake District	16. Yarmouth	27. Weymouth	38. Midhurst
7. Newcastle	17. Cotswolds	28. Christchurch	39. Bognor
8. Isle of Man	18. Cambridge	29. Ringwood	40. Brighton
9. Kirkby Lonsdale	19. Oxford	30. Salisbury	41. Lewes
10. Black Hambleton	20. Ilfracombe	31. Bartley	42. Weald
Hills	21. Bath	32. Lyndhurst	43. Boulogne

Father Lyell then took a fourteen year lease of Bartley Lodge on the fringe of the New Forest, Hampshire, seven miles west of Southampton and two north of Lyndhurst. Here he was to remain for twenty-eight years before returning permanently to Kinnordy. Bartley Lodge stood in its own grounds of eighty acres, seventy of which were laid down, without enclosure, under grass, said to furnish the best hay of the county for hunters. As Lyndhurst was the home of the New Forest Hounds this suited admirably. Fine old oaks, singly and in groups, added to the beauty of the park. Around it lay the untamed scenery of the Forest. Little wonder that Charles soon came to revel in its charms.

One of his earliest recollections, persisting into manhood, concerned an incident which occurred when he was four and a half years old. The family had set out for Kinnordy where they were to spend the summer. In the carriage with father and mother sat Charles and Tom. Behind followed a post-chaise with sisters Fanny and Marianne (just a baby), two nursemaids, and a cook. Within a stage and a half of Edinburgh, on a narrow road following the contours of a steep hillside, a flock of sheep stampeded the horses of the chaise resulting in its overturn. Little harm was done to the occupants; but in the excitement of the moment the two brothers, left alone, were able to plunder buns stored in the pockets of their equipage. It must be added that, while remembering the accident, Charles, grown up, had to rely on others for the bunny part of this story.

When almost eight years of age Charles was sent, along with Tom, to a school on the outskirts of the small town of Ringwood, a dozen miles west-southwest of Bartley, but still in Hampshire. The situation was delightful with a large meadow for playground, and the Christchurch Avon close at hand for bathing. There were about fifty pupils in all, among whom the two Lyells and three other small boys were the youngest. Before long a quarrel arose between the schoolboys and the 'blackguards', in school parlance, of the town. A challenge was delivered and accepted, and sticks agreed upon as weapons. A council of war at the school decided that the five little ones were too small to be soldiers; but the rest, on the appointed day, marched fully armed to meet the foe. Blows were heavy until news of the affray brought the master and some tradesmen to separate the combatants, with of course condign punishment to follow.

Smuggling games, though less drastic, were equally symptomatic of the troubled times. For them the school divided into two, the customs-house officers and the contrabandists laden with kegs.

The uneasy Peace of Amiens, signed in 1802, had scarcely lasted for a year. It was now 1805. Napoleon was encamped at Boulogne, waiting in vain for Villeneuve's squadron to cover his invasion. Father Lyell had accepted a captaincy in the volunteers, and his corps had been ordered to Ringwood—a pleasant event for his two sons. Then came the sad-glorious news of Trafalgar, with bonfires crowning all the hills, and yet with the outside of nearly every candle in the township blackened in mourning for Nelson.

Charles was greatly influenced in these Ringwood days by one of the other youngsters called Montague, a lad of many parts. Puzzled one Sunday by what he had heard in church, he asked Montague to explain the meaning of 'beating down Satan under our feet'. Montague, never at a loss, took his little squad to a shallow pool in which, after doffing shoes and stockings, he jumped about splashing his audience from head to foot. 'That', he said, 'is beating down Satan.' Charles did not doubt his leader's explanation at the time, but for years afterwards he wondered why water had been chosen for the illustration. He himself had equated Satan with satin.

The summer holidays always brought Charles and Tom back for the haymaking; and it was a great pleasure to join in this splendid game with their sisters Fanny and Marianne. Another excitement was provided by the felling of oak trees to build men-of-war at Portsmouth. Thousands of splendid oaks were cut down near Lyndhurst, and many beech trees too, since houses in the king's forest had a right to a certain share of firewood. It was estimated that forty acres of the best soil for oaks were required to build a single seventy-four-gun-ship, if the oaks taken were a century old and left behind them a fair proportion of younger trees. The planning of the fall of a chosen specimen, so as to cause a minimum of damage to survivors, was a matter for skilled craftsmanship; but the final blow was often left to one or other of the young Lyells.

The Ringwood school offered little in the way of education; and its boys were socially of a 'very mixed kind'. So father Lyell decided to move his sons in 1806 to Dr Radcliffe's in Salisbury, on the same Avon but sixteen miles farther north and across into Wiltshire. The doctor was a good Oxonian classical scholar, and he had two capable ushers to help with his fifty boys; and, what evidently appealed quite strongly, among these boys were representatives of the 'very best families in Wilts, Dorset, and part of Hants.'

At Ringwood, studies had been confined to English. At Salisbury, Charles, now entering his tenth year, began Latin grammar, 'which, disagreeable as it is, is considered by most schoolboys as a piece of promotion when they first begin it'. However, lack of further stimulus led to his learning very little during his two years at Salisbury. In after life he was of opinion that English girls were better educated than their brothers because they had not had to waste time in acquiring a dead language.

Though Radcliffe was a good scholar, what most im-

Plate 1   Charles Lyell.   A drawing by George Richmond which now belongs to the National Portrait Gallery in London.

Plate 2 Lyell's birth-place, Kinnordy House, near Kirriemuir.

Plate 3 Bartley Lodge in the New Forest. The wings have been added since Lyell's day.

pressed his pupils was the fact that Mrs Radcliffe was the third in succession; which naturally won for him the name of Bluebeard—number four came a few years later. The ushers too, though admittedly capable, were given to favouritism, which led to unhappy reprisals. According to Charles, too much time was allotted to sleep, with the result that many of the best sports were played at night. The most active was well organized bolster fighting; but more interesting was the training of field mice. These docile creatures were hidden during the day in boxes under the boys' beds; but when night came they were marshalled for instruction. They soon learnt to hold small pieces of wood between their forepaws, and to shoulder, ground, and present arms at the word of command. This procedure was borrowed from daytime drill conducted twice weekly by a sergeant in the small school yard.

The yard just mentioned was a poor compensation for the spacious meadow of Ringwood; and school walks, twice or thrice a week, were paraded in crocodile formation along suburban streets. Old Sarum, however, lay only a couple of miles to the north, within easy reach of a holiday excursion. A great stronghold in Romano-British times, it had later been adopted as the home of Wessex kings, and later still as the site of an influential bishopric. The boys enjoyed its splendid prehistoric camp standing on a singularly isolated hill of chalk. Down the steep opposing slopes of its triple trench they would roll great flints to meet and break, sometimes revealing sparkling quartz within.

Old Sarum had another interest in those days. It was a notorious example of a rotten borough, that is of a town whose parliamentary representation lay in the pocket of the Sovereign or of some other patron. Its ale-house with attached tea gardens sent two members to parliament as against Manchester's none. Not long before it had been bought by a peer at full political price; but it was to retain this relict

B

value only till the passing of the Reform Act of 1832.

Charles had a bad attack of measles in his first year at Salisbury, and another illness threatening consumption in his second. He was accordingly taken home for three months to recuperate. It was at this time that he made his first sally into natural history. He started collecting butterflies and moths, which he identified from pictures in his father's books. Beauty first attracted him, until presently as a collector he came to value rarity above good looks. He found much pleasure, too, in rearing caterpillars and in watching their transformations. The books he used for little else than obtaining a name and an estimate of frequency; but in these directions he went far, for, while still a boy, he could distinguish accurately several hundred species, some very minute. He also learnt by observation many of the insect time-tables, both seasonal and diurnal. His interest soon spread to water insects, especially well represented in a pond filling a clay-pit, the source of the bricks of which Bartley Lodge was built. These creatures offered specially favourable opportunities for meditative observation in the open.

In the home circle Charles's preoccupation in natural history found little favour. He had only one active ally, the head livery servant, who in past years had been successfully employed by father Lyell in hunting for botanical rarities. Occasionally this good fellow was able to join in a trip to the forest; and always his sympathy was assured. The housemaids, on the other hand, merely expressed disapproval of the smell that came from the basin in poor Charles's bedroom, used for an aquarium. The governess too complained that hats should not be broken catching insects; but her criticism was constructive, for she knitted a small net of string. Help also came from an aunt, who donated an unwanted piece of furniture which had drawers of softish wood. Henceforth the treasures caught were pinned in place, instead of being pressed between sheets of paper like plants in a herbarium; and in after years some of them proved of service to a specialist in distribution. The general feeling among grown-ups beyond the family was that Charles ought to turn to the more manly pursuits of other boys. As for these latter, they thoroughly despised all branches of natural history other than bird-nesting. Accordingly poor sensitive Charles indulged in his pleasures by stealth, keeping them secret so far as might be. He had, however, one main consolation besides the livery servant's loyalty: surely the expensive books on entomology, which he found in his father's library, full of plates and some of them written in Latin, proved that learned sages had devoted much time to its study.

We have in this discussion of Charles's entry into natural history continued beyond the recuperation period in his Salisbury schooldays. What started in that fortunate interval remained his holiday pastime to the end of his boyhood; and it would be useless to attempt to separate its prosecution into periods. Also we have reproduced the sad picture of discouragement as he himself presented it humorously in after years to amuse his fiancée. It is, no doubt, intentionally overdrawn. His published correspondence with his sisters shows that throughout life they took a keen and knowledgeable interest in flowers and butterflies.

1810-15 Finish of Schooling

After Salisbury there was an interregnum of nearly half a year, during which Charles and Tom remained at home. Their father taught them Latin, and a master called twice a week to give lessons in French; and progress was satisfactory.

At length it was decided to send the boys to Winchester; but it was found that application should have been made two years in advance. Accordingly they were entered at the ancient grammar school of the rotten borough of Midhurst (Fig. 1) in Sussex, on the Rother, eleven miles north of Chichester. The Headmaster, Dr Bayley, had formerly been an under-master at Winchester, and had modelled his school on Winchester lines. He was also an Oxonian, and had married the cousin of a bishop; and if he no longer moved in 'good society' it was only because there was 'no society' in rotten Midhurst. The school itself was beautifully situated opposite the park of Cowdray Castle. There were some seventy boys.

Schooling at Midhurst was a great change from what it had been at Ringwood and Salisbury: in the way of life, for the worse; in the way of instruction, for the better. Human relations among the boys were regulated by the law of the jungle. In the struggle for power, Charles wrote afterwards to his fiancée

each learns at last to know his master, a supremacy which depends partly on spirit, or as they term it *pluck*, and in part on physical strength. There are always some pugnacious fellows who rather delight in affrays, and in setting others on, and are the dread of the weak quiet-spirited youngsters. They are often bullies, who are afraid of many of their own age and strength, and are hated as tyrants by the weaker and younger in the school.

It is difficult for a schoolboy to know how other schools are run. The tendency is to judge from one's own experience, and to consider them all good, all bad, or all indifferent. We therefore need not accept Charles's opinion as unbiased when he wrote:

Whatever some may say or sing of the happy recollections of their school days, I believe the generality, if they told the truth, would not like to have them over again, or would consider them less happy than those to follow. I felt for the first time that I had to fight my own way in a rough world, and must depend entirely on my own resources.

It is certain that conditions as bad as those endured at Midhurst prevailed in some South of England schools as late at any rate as the nineties of last century; but these schools were quite likely exceptional.

When Charles arrived with Tom at Midhurst it was 1810, and he was already twelve years old. To begin with, according to an established kindly mitigating custom, one of the seniors lent him protection; but this was withdrawn in the second term on the ground that he was old enough in years and school experience to fend for himself. Lack of resistance at first encouraged even juniors to attack; but before the term was through the worm turned (a rather awkward metaphor considering the reason) when a 'vulgar low sort of a boy' knocked him to earth. 'Annoyed beyond measure by this ignominious occurrence', Charles let it be known that he would 'like to see him try it again'. There followed the almost inevitable fight for position that was expected some time or other of every boy of the school. This particular fight was spread over two days, lasting on each occasion for five or six hours, with two-minute rounds and one-minute intervals. Charles won in the sense that he finished able to walk with assistance, whereas his opponent had to go to bed. This spared him much molestation in the future; but school opinion was not very enthusiastic about the result, holding that the vulgar fellow was handicapped in the matter of age and height to an extent that counterbalanced his having had previous lessons in boxing.

A short time after this, an even more desperate battle took place between two of the biggest boys of the school. 'It lasted three days, and was a most savage concern. The pluck with which they fought on, after both had grown pale with the blood lost from the nose, and black with bruises, was a sight that [Charles thought both] barbarous and brutal; but the eager enjoyment and admiration of the school at their *pluck* was surprising.'

Repugnant as much of the jungle law appeared to Charles, he was ready to admit certain compensations. 'Some boys,' he said, 'quite sink under this roughing, but in general they become more manly and hardier.' Against this is the great disadvantage that a bullied junior is only too likely to develop into a bullying senior.

Other items of communal life included football, cricket, and fives, but these were apt to be deserted, and studies too, in a craze for draughts and later chess, played for small stakes. When money failed, breakfast was pledged, and this led on to petty larceny. On one occasion Charles, fearing detection, covered his face and bolted out knocking over the approaching purveyor, milk jug and all. He escaped identification; but the trouble was reported to the prefects who ordained that in future no boy was to pay away more than half his breakfast on any one day.

At the end of the second year a new hobby came, and we presently find Charles leading an orchestra of eight flutes, three fifes, triangles, and tambourines.

It has been noted above that bird-nesting was the only branch of nature study recognized as permissible by Charles's schoolmates. Here he excelled, and got to know the eggs of almost every bird in the countryside, and of these there was a great variety. Some, however, of his activity was far from innocent, for he spent much of his time, especially when he got a chance on Sunday, in hunting for the eggs of partridges and pheasants on neighbouring estates. It was a great game country, and the eggs made an excellent supplement to breakfast.

As regards more formal education, methods of marking and consequent promotion, borrowed from Winchester, introduced a lively sense of competition that suited Charles's temperament admirably. At the end of his first year, he received a prize for English recitation; and every year afterwards he was similarly successful, until high enough

in the school to carry off prizes for Latin and English composition. When he had risen to the second class (from the
top) he ventured upon a poem in the versification of Scott's
Lady of the Lake, instead of in the standard heroic couplet.
Dr Bayley accepted it, but with the injunction not to do it
again.

Also in the second class he wrote a mock-heroic in Latin
modelled on Homer's battle of frogs and mice. The subject
was an actual invasion of the school by water-rats following
upon the draining of a pond along the side of the playground. It was an ambitious undertaking, running to thirty-
eight verses, and it not only seized on the imagination of
his schoolmates, but also enlisted the anonymous help of
an under-master, who corrected certain grammatical errors.
Presented in this doctored form to the Head, it received
high praise for the correctitude of its Latin, and a repetition
of the injunction not to do it again.

We have now seen Charles through his schooldays. He
had arrived at the top class before leaving in June 1815,
the month of Waterloo. His autobiographical sketch, prepared for his fiancée, ceases to give any detail before this
date is reached; but we have reproduced enough of its story
to appreciate his early apprenticeship to natural history and
literature. Tom had already left Midhurst, probably in
1812, to join the navy.

Chapter 2

Geological Background

After leaving Midhurst Charles matriculated before his eighteenth birthday at Exeter College, Oxford (Fig. 1), whither he went the following January, 1816. He had already found in his father's library a copy of Robert Bakewell's *Introduction to Geology*, published in 1813. This, according to his sister-in-law, Mrs Henry Lyell (*née* Katherine M. Horner), 'was the first book which gave him an idea of the existence of such a science as geology, and something said in it about the antiquity of the earth excited his imagination so much that he was well prepared to take an interest in the lectures of Dr Buckland, Professor of Geology at Oxford, who was then at the height of his popularity'. It therefore seems appropriate to devote the present chapter to an outline of the state of the geological world into which Charles, or Lyell as we shall henceforward call him, was introduced by Bakewell's volume.

Robert Bakewell is not ranked among the great geologists of all time; but his book shows him to have been a very sensible fellow and intensely keen on his subject. He was a geological consultant, who furnished landlords with reports on the mineral and soil prospects of their estates, coupled with accounts of 'objects of curiosity, natural history, or science'. His well balanced interest in regard to the economic and non-economic aspects of geology places him in the same category as William Smith, Richard Griffith, De la Beche, the Prince Consort, and Werner, to mention but a few approximate contemporar-

14

ies. His book was much appreciated, and by 1838 had gone through five editions in this country, two in America and one, translated, in Germany. We shall return to it presently.

Meanwhile let us note that geology, as might be expected, had gradual beginnings. It is pleasing and profitable to recall how various important aspects were more or less realized by one observer or another, sometimes even in the remote past. In Chapter 8 we shall review the history of research which Lyell himself has furnished in the first volume of his *Principles*. Meanwhile, as it is universally acknowledged that the actual birth-pangs of the science date from the end of the eighteenth century and the beginning of the nineteenth, let us concentrate upon this eventful period.

A vigorous, sometimes unseemly, struggle between the followers of James Hutton (1726-97) of Edinburgh and Abraham Gottlob Werner (1749-1817) of Freiberg in Saxony focused attention upon interpretation of earth history. The result arrived at during Lyell's boyhood was somewhat curious. Public opinion shifted increasingly away from Werner's doctrines towards acceptance of many of Hutton's, but with a very important reservation. Thus, while most geologists came to admit that Hutton, along with others, had been right in recognizing basalt as igneous, and that he, in advance of all others, had been justified in extending this conception to granite, very few accepted his master doctrine of the uniformity of geological processes in past and present ages. In other words, there were many Vulcanists who admitted ancient volcanoes, and many Plutonists who recognized granite as a consolidated melt, but most of these Vulcanists and Plutonists were Catastrophists—scarcely any were Uniformitarians. As we have already pointed out, Lyell was to liquidate this vitally important reservation. He was also to play a major part in splitting the Tertiary Group into component systems. This last was a stratigraphical achievement based upon the principle of successive faunas established by three juniors of the Hutton-Werner period, namely William Smith (1769-1839), Georges Cuvier (1769-1832), and Alexandre Brongniart (1770-1847). Lyell came to know all three of them personally.

Hutton and Werner

Let us now give a slight sketch of Hutton and his life-work. He studied medicine at Edinburgh, Paris, and Leiden, at which last he graduated M.D. in 1749, the year of Werner's birth. He never practised, but, having a good prospect of an income from early experiments on distillation of sal ammoniac from soot, he decided on agriculture as a career. In 1752 he went to Norfolk for experience, and made many journeys on foot to different parts of England, discovering *en route* what an interesting subject geology is. After an excursion to Holland, Belgium, and Picardy, he returned to Scotland in 1754, and settled on a farm in Berwickshire inherited from his father. Here he continued to take a keen interest in geology, and in 1764 made a geological tour of the Highlands. In 1768 he let his farm and settled in Edinburgh to enjoy with less interruption the society of his intellectual friends.

The first publication of Hutton's long deliberations we owe to the establishment of the Royal Society of Edinburgh in 1783. His paper, the *Theory of the Earth*, was read in 1785 and published in the first volume of the Society's *Transactions* in 1788. The re-publication of the *Theory* in book form in 1795 was a response to an attack by Richard Kirwan, later to become President of the Royal Irish Academy. The twelve years which elapsed between the appearance of the *Theory* as a paper and as a book provided Hutton with opportunity for six important geological excursions, on which he was accompanied by one or more of his personal friends.

Hutton's uniformitarianism was inspired by recognition, as he thought, of divine design in nature. 'The purpose of the earth', he assures us, 'is evidently to maintain vegetable and animal life' for the benefit of mankind. Accordingly he held that the earth must be running on perfect principles, which, being perfect, can know no change. At the same time he interpreted his conception of no change with considerable flexibility: 'We are not to limit Nature with the uniformity of an equable progression.' 'It is our business to learn of Nature (that is by observation) the ways and means which in her wisdom are adopted.' This is an injunction with which any modern geologist may well be satisfied.

Animal life is dependent on plant life; plant life upon soil; and soil originates through disintegration of solid rock. Once solid rock disintegrates, its debris falls a prey to streams and rivers and is carried slowly but surely to the sea. The various processes of erosion are observable realities; and, considered in reference to the actual details of landscape, they are found to be related as cause is to effect. Two important thoughts follow immediately: one is the immensity of time required to develop a landscape, when progress is so slow that Roman roads are still traceable across British hills; the other is the inevitable end to which erosion seems to be trending, namely the obliteration of all dry land.

Obliteration, however, is not inevitable. There is in fact abundant evidence of reconstruction. Hutton early recognized, probably quite independently of help from others, that many solid rocks now exposed to view originated on the sea bottom as the waste of older rocks or as accumulations of organic remains. Here then is a welcome indication of a cyclic operation, with reconstruction counterbalancing destruction; but two questions present themselves: What has led to the consolidation of these marine deposits? How is it that they are no longer covered by the sea?

In consolidation, Hutton, after considering and dismissing cement as a significant factor, thought that he could recognize the operation of heat in association with pressure. His views in this matter are now largely discarded; but it is enough for his theory if we admit, as most of us do, that subterranean heat has played a vital rôle in developing crystalline schists. Having recognized deep-seated heat (the evidence afforded by mines had not as yet been realized), Hutton proceeded to suggest that it provided motive power responsible for the elevation of marine formations to the considerable heights at which we often find them. It is fair to paraphrase this conclusion and say that Hutton's *Theory* pictures the earth as a heat-engine— Hutton, it must be remembered was a friend of James Watt. Volcanoes Hutton regarded as the safety valves of his engine.

It may be suggested that Hutton might have derived his heat-engine theory from a comparison of the widespread basalt of his native land with the products of active volcanoes, instead of adopting a much more circuitous and hazardous line of argument based on the consolidation of sediments; but, says Hutton, 'when first I conceived my theory, naturalists were far from suspecting that basaltic rocks were of volcanic origin; I could not then have employed an argument from these rocks as I do now.' This remark of Hutton's suggests a comparison of his dates with those of the great Frenchman Nicolas Desmarest. Hutton developed his *Theory*, including the igneous origin of basalt, somewhere about 1760, read his paper in 1785, and published in 1788. Desmarest realized the volcanic origin of columnar basalt in Auvergne (and, by analogy, in the far-away cliffs of the Giant's Causeway) in 1763, read his paper in 1765, and published in 1774. (The actual discovery of the Auvergne volcanoes belongs to Jean Etienne Guettard, 1752; but he regarded columnar basalt as 'formed by crystallization in an aqueous fluid'.)

Hutton realized the igneous nature of granite from its unstratified crystalline appearance in hand specimen. His delight can readily be imagined when, in 1785, he saw granite veins cutting mica-schist in Glen Tilt. This proved to his satisfaction that the granite material had been injected in a molten condition; and similar observations followed elsewhere. Alternative interpretations have indeed been advanced right up to the present day, but I for one accept Hutton's deduction as fully justified.

Archibald Geikie has claimed Hutton as the Father of Modern Geology. It is therefore interesting to make a second comparison of dates, to see where he stands in relation to other representative founders of the Age of Science: Newton, 1642-1727; Linnaeus, 1707-78; Hutton, 1726-97; Watt, 1736-1819; Lavoisier, 1743-94; Faraday, 1791-1867. His contemporaneity with Lavoisier, for whom he had a great admiration though himself a phlogistonist, has a peculiar interest. (The phlogistonists held that escape of a practically imponderable substance, which they called phlogiston, was the essential feature of combustion, whereas Lavoisier regarded combination with oxygen as fundamental. Looking back it is possible to equate Hutton's phlogiston fairly closely with the heat and light energy of later scientists.) Lyell has pointed out that the bitterness with which Hutton's novel ideas were received was partly due to the current political situation. His *Theory*, confidently interpreting God's purpose through thoughtful observation of Nature without accepting guidance from revelation, was considered subversive. It appeared as a paper in 1788 and in book form in 1795. The French

Revolution lasted from 1789 to 1795, and removed Lavoisier's head in 1794.

Hutton during his life won the interest and support, sometimes only partial, of a few gifted friends. He was a writer of fine sentences, but his publications taken as a whole are almost unreadable. Fortunately one of his friends, the mathematician and physicist Professor John Playfair (1748-1819), decided to present the *Theory* in more attractive form. As a result there appeared in 1802 the *Illustrations of the Huttonian Theory*, a masterpiece of lucidity. One important difference of approach may be gathered from a comparison of the two following quotations. What is the final cause of the universal waste we see about us? asks Hutton—'Is it in order to destroy the system of this living world that the operations of nature are thus disposed? Or is it to perpetuate the progress of that system which, in other respects, appears to be contrived with so much wisdom? Here are questions which a Theory of the Earth must solve; and here, indeed, must be found the most material part by far of any Theory of the Earth.' 'To trace the series of these revolutions', Playfair quietly answers, 'to examine their causes, and thus to connect together all the indications of change that are found in the mineral kingdom, is the proper object of a Theory of the Earth.'

Let us now turn to Werner, whose dates (1749-1817) show him an almost exact contemporary of Playfair. Werner came of a family with a three hundred years' connection with mining in Saxony—a region which for centuries had functioned as a dispersal centre for mining technique. We are reminded of this last by the quaint name of 'toadstone' still attached to Carboniferous lavas in the metalliferous field of Derbyshire. It is thought that early German miners classed these rocks as *tot*, or dead, from the point of view of mineralization.

Werner saw the whole world through mineral spectacles.

Scenery, industry, population, civilization, architecture, sculpture, agriculture, commerce, and war are all regulated by mineral distribution; and Werner delighted to proclaim the fact with an eloquence which proved irresistible. In 1775 he was appointed Inspector and Teacher of Mining and Mineralogy at the recently instituted Mining Academy at Freiberg (Fig. 10). The result was amazing. Cuvier has recorded how:

At the little Academy, founded for the purpose of training mining engineers and mine captains for the mines of Saxony, there was renewed the spectacle presented by the universities of the Middle Ages, for students flocked thither from every civilized country. One saw men from the most remote countries, already well advanced in years, men of education holding important positions, engaged with all diligence in the study of the German language, that they might fit themselves to sit at the feet of this 'Great Oracle of the Sciences of the Earth'.

Werner made a determinate language his first objective. He understood that no progress was possible until people could express themselves in words. He addressed himself to mineral classification, following the example of Linnaeus, who, however, had applied himself more especially to the classification of plants and animals. Both these men aroused exceptional enthusiasm among their pupils, who felt in their presence that order was developing out of chaos. One realizes on glancing through Werner's mineral classification that it would often enable a student to name a specimen, an essential step towards scientific intercourse; and, when he passed from minerals to rocks, Werner still regarded precise classification as a prime necessity.

It is in interpretation that Werner failed. For one thing he regarded active volcanoes as mere modern accidents due to spontaneous combustion of coal seams lying near the surface. They had no counterparts in the geological past. For him, all rocks, apart from unimportant terrestrial accumulations, had been deposited in the ocean, with characters dependent upon world-wide changes in the extent and composition of the same. Accordingly his followers were nicknamed Neptunists.

Werner's scheme of nature at first read as follows:

(1) In *Primitive* times a universal ocean; no detritus; all deposits chemical and very irregularly accumulated; granite the first crystallization.

(2) In *Transition* times a decrease of ocean; crests of primitive mountains appear; detritus mingles with chemical deposit; enough of chemical ingredients to consolidate gathering sediment with steep dip on submerged slopes; life begins.

(3) In *Floetz* times a further decrease of ocean; flanking ridges of transitional rocks exposed; detrital and organic deposits begin to predominate over chemical; thus more or less horizontal stratification is alone possible (*floetz* means flat); organic life advances in type.

(4) Ocean falls to approximately present-day limits; present-day conditions prevail with little chemical deposit except calc-sinter and bog-iron-ore.

In 1788 Werner was compelled to add to his original scheme a Newest Floetz-Trap (Basalt) Formation, requiring the assumption of a general deluge, the waters of which disappeared as mysteriously as they had come. He had already from 1776 taught the non-volcanic origin of basalt after examining a Saxon exposure. He seems to have known, at the time, of Desmarest's claim of 1774, but he himself 'found not a trace of volcanic action, nor the smallest proof of volcanic origin'.

As regards point (1) of the above list, Werner's school discounted Hutton's granite veins as secondary phenomena unconnected with the universal primitive granite of their creed; and as regards (2) they treated consolidation of sedi-

Plate 4 Fingal's Cave, Staffa.

Plate 5 Reconstruction of an iguanodon.

ments as an original cementation feature dating from deposition, and did not accept Hutton's view that steep dips and faults are subsequent phenomena due to earth movement.

It happened that Edinburgh became the main battlefield in the Hutton-Werner war. The local leader of the Wernerians was Robert Jameson (1774–1854), who, after considerable field and laboratory research, went in 1800 to Freiberg to perfect his knowledge of the great master's teaching. He returned to Edinburgh in 1804 and was forthwith appointed to the vacant chair of Natural History, which he occupied for the next fifty years. He was a broad-minded and diligent worker, and his classes, though leading to no university examination, were well attended. He had many distinguished students, some from abroad; and for the most part they seem to have felt greatly indebted to their Professor, though many of them arrived at true interpretations of igneous rocks well in advance of his conversion. Thus we find Ami Boué, destined to become one of France's leading geologists, publishing in 1825 in Jameson's own *Edinburgh Philosophical Journal* the following appreciation of the position:

(1) All geologists accept extinct volcanoes.
(2) Most accept Tertiary basalt as volcanic.
(3) Many accept the trap of the Secondaries.
(4) Some (including Boué) regard granite, syenite, and porphyries as igneous.

Jameson's acquiescence to the publication of this reckoning, while he himself was still Wernerian, bespeaks fair-mindedness; but there can be no question of the real bad feeling among the many contestants. 'I have myself known', says Geikie in his *Founders of Geology*, 'a number of men who remembered the acrimony of the warfare, and some of whom even played the part of combatants in

c

the struggle.' It was a strange experience for myself, more than forty years Geikie's junior, to witness a lingering survival of the bitterness. In 1921 the British Association met in Edinburgh, and a local committee was appointed to prepare a small volume entitled *Edinburgh's Place in Scientific Progress*. In a geological contribution I ventured to recall that Jameson, in recognition of his many services to the scientific life of the city, including his development of a great museum, was awarded a civic funeral. This paragraph of mine was excised, and in its place was inserted the well-known contemptuous judgment of Charles Darwin, who in 1826, as an impetuous boy of eighteen, shared the general opinion that Jamesons' continued fight against vulcanism was outmoded. It was all very interesting.

1807 The Geological Society of London

This mention of Darwin has taken us beyond Lyell's schooldays. Let us return to 1807 marked by the foundation of the Geological Society of London, the first of its kind in the world. To begin with the Society was a dining club of well-to-do men, most of whom had mineral cabinets of their own and took a special interest in chemistry. The illustrious Humphry Davy typifies this group; but we also find among the thirteen founder-members James Parkinson, author of *Organic Remains of a Former World*, 1804-11, and William Phillips, who was to do yeoman service to the science in his *Selection of Facts arranged to form an Outline of the Geology of England and Wales*, 1818, expanded in partnership with William Daniel Conybeare in 1822— with simplified title.

Out of sight of the Castle Rock, Salisbury Crags, Arthur's Seat and all the other igneous hills of Edinburgh, the young Society was impatient of the tumult that came to them from the north. Still its members were anxious to hear both sides of questions in dispute, and at their second meeting they elected as Honorary Members Playfair, Kirwan, and Jameson. Probably in the same spirit they also elected John Josias Conybeare (brother of W. D.) and Joseph Townsend, who, with Parkinson and William Phillips, took an interest in fossils and stratigraphy.

The Beginnings of Stratigraphy

The majority feeling at this time seems to have been quite cool towards William Smith, who, as we shall see below, had already established that fossils can be used to identify stratigraphical formations from district to district. Indeed most of the members may not have known of his existence. They elected and re-elected as their President (1807-13, 1818-20, 1833-5) George Bellas Greenough, who had studied under Werner, and commissioned him to produce a Wernerian map of England and Wales. (It became Smithian before it appeared in 1820.) Also, their first Secretary collected a fund to employ a Geneva Wernerian Jean François Berger (a political exile) to report on Devonshire, Cornwall, the Isle of Man, and northern Ireland. The Wernerians vaguely recognized a fossil succession, starting with animals of low organization; but they did not use this idea as a guide to stratigraphy. Instead, they put first things first, and expected lithology to reveal the world-wide succession of changes in oceanic composition and extent, which their master had taught them was fundamental. Accordingly, unlike the Board of Agriculture, the Royal Institution, and the Society of Arts, Manufactures and Commerce, not to mention Sir Joseph Banks, perennial President of the Royal Society, the Geological Society as such took no steps to help Smith in completing and publishing his geological map of England and Wales, which at last appeared in 1815.

William Smith (1769-1839) was a genius born in the same year as Cuvier, Napoleon, and Wellington. He was also a plain practical man, a civil engineer particularly interested in surveying routes for canals. When he left the world, he was little richer than when he entered, largely because of his 'perfect contempt for money when compared with science'. His identification of formations by their fossil contents became widely known, more particularly in England, after Townsend in 1799 had taken down to dictation the formations found around Bath, from the Coal up to the Chalk, along with a selection of their characteristic fossils.

Fig. 2 William Smith

His first geologically coloured map was also of the Bath district, and dated 1799. His findings appeared in print in 1801, but were familiar to many in advance, for Townsend circulated copies of his 1799 list, and Smith himself publicly demonstrated maps and sections, particularly at agricultural shows. At last on 1 August 1815, 'after 24 years of intense application', as he tells us in the accompanying memoir, he produced his marvellous stratigraphical map of England and Wales, on the scale of five miles to an inch! It was a good date, for he was able to rejoice 'how the wisdom and vigour of His Majesty's Councils have given peace to a distracted world, and may render this happy event the commencement of a new era in the history of natural science'. One is left to wonder whether this sentence was penned before or after Napoleon's escape from Elba, for Waterloo was not won till the 18th of June.

The following quotations from his *Stratigraphical System of Organized Fossils* (pp. vii, ix) which appeared two years later, sufficiently indicate Smith's views as to the origin of faunal successions and the importance that he attached to their aid in deciphering stratigraphy:

Each layer of these fossil organized bodies must be considered as a separate creation or how could the earth be formed *stratum super stratum*, and each with a different race of animals?

Identification of Strata by the help of organized Fossils becomes one of the most important modern discoveries in Geology. It enables the Geologist clearly to distinguish one Stratum from another in Britain, and also to trace their connexion with the same Strata on the Continent.

Organized fossils are to the naturalist as coins to the antiquary; they are the antiquities of the earth, and very distinctly show its gradual regular formation with the various changes of inhabitants in the watery element.

To help in the recognition of these invaluable guides Smith published *Strata identified by Organised Fossils* in 1816. It carries beautiful coloured illustrations of 158 specimens, presumably prepared by James Sowerby.

Starting in 1806, Georges Cuvier (1769-1832) and Alexandre Brongniart (1770-1847), independently of Smith, established a fossil succession which they described in their celebrated *Essai sur la géographie minéralogique des environs de Paris*. This furnishes an account of the Tertiaries of the Paris Basin, and a preliminary abstract was published in 1810. Both authors were of outstanding ability. Cuvier has rightly been called the Founder of Comparative Vertebrate Anatomy. Brongniart was a leading mineralogist as well as conchologist. As regards environment they had similar advantages to those enjoyed by Smith, for they lived in the midst of a well exposed, highly fossiliferous succession of rocks endowed with marked lithological contrasts. They had the further advantage that Jean Baptiste de Lamarck (1744–1829) was concurrently naming and classifying the invertebrates of the Paris Tertiaries, and comparing them with modern analogues. It was immaterial for the establishment of the fossil sequence that Cuvier and Lamarck interpreted its origin very differently. Cuvier like Smith considered that each fauna in turn was a new creation, and he cleared the decks for its arrival by invoking some catastrophic revolution. Lamarck on the other hand, like Erasmus Darwin, was an evolutionist. He has perhaps never received full credit for recognizing the fact of evolution because he advocated causes which seem unacceptable, including inheritance of acquired characters— Darwin followed suit, but is forgiven because he gave much more weight to natural selection.

When I think of Lamarck my mind goes back to the battle of the Somme. I had noticed some bricks in the side of a trench, the only relic of the village of Bazantin, northeast of Albert. Someone unknown paused beside me: 'This', he said, 'was the birthplace of Lamarck'; and on he went.

All the four characters, Smith, Cuvier, Brongniart, and Lamarck will appear again in subsequent chapters. Meanwhile it is time to return to Bakewell's *Introduction*. Bakewell started as a Wernerian, and is very careful to present facts before theories, or, to use Wernerian terms, to attend to geognosy before attempting geology. When, however, he does come to discussion of hypotheses he is emphatic in his criticism of one point after another of Werner's doctrines. His final comment is reserved for his glossary of geological terms, where we find that ' "well educated geognost" as used by some writers denotes a perfect disciple of Werner, who has lost the use of his own eyes by constantly looking through the eyes of his master'. The most disappointing feature of Bakewell's book is that even in the 1838 edition he makes no mention of the amazing achievement of his business rival, William Smith.

Älter rother Sandstein. Now let us close with mention of two representative stratigraphical mistakes, one of which has left its mark to this day.

(1) The flat formations of Saxony and of Scotland both begin with a red sandstone. Jameson in 1808 hesitatingly (but wrongly as it turned out) suggested a correlation (*System of Mineralogy*, vol. 3, p. 159). Werner had called the Saxon sandstone either Rothe tode Liegende (meaning the red barren formation underlying the metalliferous Zechstein Limestone), or else Älter rother Sandstein (old red sandstone, older that is than the Zechstein). Accordingly Jameson introduced the name Old Red Sandstone for its supposed Scottish equivalent. Though the mistake was fairly soon rectified, the name has stuck.

(2) Similarly in 1818 Bakewell sought Saxon equivalents. He rightly correlated the Magnesian Limestone east of the Pennines with the Zechstein; but, finding no reappearance of this limestone west of the Pennines, he wrongly concluded that all formations seen between its outcrop and the Irish Sea must be pre-Zechstein. Thus he misinterpreted the Cheshire Trias as a facies of the Millstone Grit, and grouped the two together as Old Red Sandstone (in Werner's sense). In this scheme the Mountain

Limestone figured as top member of the underlying Transitional formations. The Yorkshire Trias Bakewell put in its proper position above the Magnesian Limestone, and so treated it as quite a different formation from the Cheshire

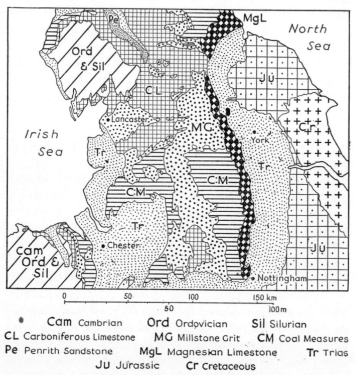

Fig. 3 Modern geological map of north-central England, to show why Bakewell correlated the Cheshire Trias with the Millstone Grit, thinking both older than the Coal Measures and Magnesian Limestone.

Trias. The two come together south of Nottingham, but this does not present an insuperable difficulty. As the Trias is unfossiliferous we might conceive of Smith making the same mistake as Bakewell. He did not, because his knowledge of the circumstances was much more thorough.

Chapter 3

Oxford with Buckland

Lyell's first year at Oxford, 1816, is covered by five published letters addressed to his father. These make no mention of natural history, but instead discuss such matters as social standing, literature, study and examinations. From one we gather that a career at the Bar is in prospect.

At an early stage Lyell announces that he has 'become acquainted with several gentlemanly men'; while a little later he confidently assumes that his liberal-minded parent will be much prejudiced in favour of a translator of *Juvenal*, who frankly confesses that 'his mother was a carpenter's daughter, and his father scarcely so respectable'. As for Exeter College, it is no longer 'entirely provincial', and the 'greatest part of those West-countrymen that remain have rubbed off their dross in our public schools'.

Lyell comments freely on literary topics, ranging from ancient to modern; and is outspoken in his condemnation of Coleridge's *Christabel* which appeared at this time. He competes for a University prize with a poem, *The Horses of Lysippus*, but is unsuccessful.

In October he is examined, and does much better than he expected. He offered mathematics and classics; and in the oral is temporarily rendered almost inarticulate by the sight of 'a great many kind friends' rushing down from the top benches to the lower to witness the ordeal at close quarters. He got through, but questions whether 'intercourse with the world' will in the future supply the confidence and quickness which his father has told him are among the chief requisites of the Bar.

We have no specific record of Lyell's activities during the first half of his second year, 1817, but, as we find him starting the long vacation with geology as his first interest, we may safely assume that it was in the previous term that he attended Professor Buckland's course of lectures. He was extremely fortunate in having the opportunity of doing so, for William Buckland (1784-1856) was one of the most delightful enthusiasts who has ever graced the science of geology. He was a complete naturalist, born at Axminster in the Lias country (Fig. 1), and a fossil collector from childhood onwards. In 1801 he won a scholarship at Oxford, and early in his residence had what he called his first lesson in field geology. The occasion was a walk to Shotover Hill; and his instructor was William John Broderip, who had learnt about fossils from Townsend, friend of William Smith. Broderip is best remembered for his subsequent discovery in the Jurassic Stonefield 'Slate' of remains correctly described as mammalian by Cuvier followed by Richard Owen.

Still it is not clear exactly when, probably by degrees, Buckland became a Smithian stratigrapher. After getting his B.A. in 1804 he attended lectures on mineralogy and chemistry by Dr John Kidd, who gathered around himself a group of keen geologists including Buckland and the brothers Conybeare; and these formed a geological club of quite unusual research activity. We have already seen how the Geological Society of London in 1807 elected the older Conybeare, J. J., at that time Professor of Anglo-Saxon, to be one of its first Honorary Members; but it was the younger Conybeare, W. D. (1787-1857), who was the mainspring of the Oxford Club. He wandered widely from Kent to the Cotswolds, following formational outcrops,

tracing their relation to scenery and noting their characteristic fossils. He was thus 'prepared', he tells us, 'to seize
the general fact of the successive distribution of the ancient
genera when first laid down as an admitted fact in the progress of geology, which was the case about this time, 1809'.
This date is a little later than one might expect, and may
possibly be inaccurate as Conybeare wrote the above long
after the event. Earlier, in 1822, in the preface to the con-
joint *Outlines*, he had told us how Smith between 1790 and
1800 'had freely communicated the information he possessed in many quarters, till in fact it became by oral dif-
fusion the common property of a large body of English
geologists, and thus contributed to the progress of the science in many quarters where the author was little known'.
Even so, we may note that Buckland did not begin annual
geological tours on horseback, as contrasted with local excursions, until 1808, so that he may not have fully realized
the persistence of fossil successions in earlier days.

From 1810 to 1815 Buckland was closely associated with
Greenough in preparing the Geological Society's map of
England, and was well aware of the stratigraphical significance of fossils. He did not, however, on this account lose
interest in Werner's classification. On the contrary, in
1816, along with Greenough and the older Conybeare, he
joined in the second end-of-the-war rush to the Continent
and called on the Oracle at his Freiberg home. The result
was a little disappointing. Werner gave them 'a grand
supper and talked learnedly of his books and music, and
anything but Geology'. Still, undeterred, Buckland drew
up a comprehensive table (published in 1818 in William
Phillips' *Outline*) suggesting comparisons between details
of the British stratigraphical sequence and possible equivalents in Werner's universal scheme. Many question
marks were inserted, but Buckland did not query the propriety of recognizing a Transition Class to separate the

British Old Red Sandstone (which he wrongly thought might perhaps correspond with the Saxon Old Red Sandstone) from a Primitive Class (with granite commonly at its base). It is significant that these so-called Transitional and Primitive formations lay outside the field of his own personal experience. Looking back, it is interesting now to realize that, owing to successive localized mountain-building episodes, of which Werner had no conception, Transitional sediments, as at first interpreted, ended in Scotland with the Silurian, in Saxony with the Carboniferous, and in the Glarus Alps with the Eocene.

Buckland followed Kidd as Reader of Mineralogy in 1813, and became Professor of Geology when a chair was endowed in 1819. He declared that he would not have stood for the former appointment if his friend Conybeare had been prepared to accept it. Actually Conybeare left Oxford the following year for a country living, apparently thinking that he could give better service as a Gilbert White of geology on a large scale, treating the whole country as his geological parish. His book, *Outlines of the Geology of England and Wales*, written in conjunction with William Phillips, was a worthy fruit of this ambition.

Buckland's main stratigraphical interests lay in the Mesozoic and later sedimentary successions, especially in regard to the Diluvium (Pleistocene) that underlies the Alluvium (Recent). Like most of his contemporaries he was a Catastrophist, considering that there had been a succession of wholesale extinctions and creations, and that the Diluvium was the product of Noah's flood. In this direction he was destined to find his most active opponent in his pupil Charles Lyell.

Before closing this introduction of one who will reappear frequently in succeeding pages, let us quote from his daughter, Mrs E. O. Gordon, some of the gossip that accumulated around his doings:

Of his adventures with that geological celebrity, Mary Ann Anning,[1] in whose company he was to be seen wading up to his knees in search of fossils in the blue lias [of Lyme Regis]; of his breakfast-table at his lodgings there, loaded with beefsteaks and belemnites, tea and terebratula, muffins and madrepores, toast and trilobites, every table and chair as well as the floor occupied by fossils whole and fragmentary, large and small, with rocks, earths, clays, and heaps of books and papers, his breakfast hour being the only time that the collectors could be sure of finding him at home, to bring their contributions and receive their pay; of his dropping his hat and handkerchief from the mail to stop the coach and secure a fossil; of the old woman who, finding him asleep on the top of the coach, relieved his pockets of a quantity of stones; of his travelling carriage, built extra strong for the heavy loads it had to carry, and fitted up on the forepart with a furnace and implements for assays and analysis.

To these I may add a couple of stories, perhaps apocryphal, at any rate not found in print: of how Buckland informed his guests one evening that they had just been eating Siberian mammoth; and of how at another dinner party he told a lady of having given temporary shelter in his hair to some foreign bugs. 'I took them out as soon as possible', he added, 'but would you believe it they were all dead?' 'Killed by the natives, I suppose', was her ready response.

Readers should also remember that Buckland's class on occasion rode to its exposures on horseback; and that in those days field geologists—like cricketers, as well as huntsmen—regularly performed in top hats.

Let us now turn to four published letters from son to father Lyell, dated from the second half of 1817. A very pleasant feature is the extent of mutual understanding which they reveal. Thus, in the following quotation which refers to a call young Lyell paid on James Sowerby, there

[1] Mary Anning was a highly successful professional collector of fossils at Lyme Regis. A stained glass window commemorates her in the village church.

was obviously no need to introduce Sowerby as a remarkable collector, describer, depicter, and salesman of fossils,
nor to explain why a particular fossil deserved the title of

Fig. 4 Young mammoth mounted in Leningrad Museum in the struggling
attitude in which it was dug out of the frozen mud of Siberia. The end of
its trunk was devoured by dogs at the time of its exhumation. Drawn by
W. J. McCallien.

the 'identical Ammonites Bucklandi'. Actually this specimen was an unusually big ammonite which had lost its
inner whorls and so had become a ring of lifebelt propor-
tions. Buckland on finding it passed his head and one
shoulder through the opening before remounting his
horse—and was promptly dubbed by his merry companions a true Ammon Knight. Sowerby to celebrate the
event called the species Bucklandi. The paragraph in the
letter reads as follows:

When searching about the Row for his house, behold the very
identical Ammonites Bucklandi was lying on the steps! I went
in and introduced myself, telling him by what means I had discovered his house. 'Ah', said he, 'little I believe did they think
at Oxford what advantage I should take of that joke. I hear

Buckland was perfectly astonished when he read it.' I exclaimed involuntarily 'Well he might be', which he took in good part, laughing heartily.

Similarly, when Lyell sends his father some verses composed after visiting Staffa (Fig. 1), he simply adds: 'Whatever you may think of the poetry, you will agree with me in regretting that Werner should have died without the knowledge of this geological discovery concerning the origin and formation of basalt.' Readers will note that Werner like Sowerby, needed no introduction, though they may be puzzled as to what is said of him: Werner had only recently died, whereas Staffa, thanks to Sir Joseph Banks, became world-famous in 1772.

Other geological features of Lyell's letters include an account of the changes in the shifty Yarmouth coastline, which he traced during a visit to friends, and of a big collection of Norfolk fossils made by a local naturalist. We find here a foretaste of what was to become his very special interest in Quaternary and Tertiary affairs.

In other directions Lyell tells his father of insect collections he has examined and of inquiries as to whether the botanical exploration of the New Forest still continues to bear fruit.

A journal, which Lyell kept, records coaching north with his father to Kinnordy in the long vacation. The most significant geological entry concerns a very deep narrow gorge in the Black Hambleton Hills (Fig. 1) of Yorkshire 'without a river (unfortunately for the Huttonians)'. It is almost certain that by this time Lyell had read Professor Playfair's luminous and eloquent *Illustrations of the Huttonian Theory*, which, Bakewell tells us in the preface to his *Introduction*, produced 'the first general impulse given to the public taste for geological investigation in this country'. In Lyell's early days Hutton's opponents, who attributed valley erosion to inundations connected with rapid earth movement rather than to ordinary rivers, seemed to have a strong case when they cited dry valleys. It was only much later that satisfactory explanations, of one kind or another, were found for these anomalies—Clement Reid, for instance, explained many of the dry valleys of the chalk country as due to river erosion under tundra conditions, when the chalk in depth was rendered impervious by frozen groundwater. Lyell for long appealed to marine erosion acting during slow upheaval or slow submergence.

Passing through Edinburgh, the Lyells called on Jameson. (They made a habit of visiting local scientists wherever they went.)

After reaching Kinnordy, Lyell examined various quarries, and then set out with two undergraduate friends bound for Staffa. They travelled by horse and boat, and one result was the poem already mentioned.

Chapter 4

Oxford and After

1818-19 Long Vacation and Graduation

Of Lyell's third year at Oxford, 1818, we know nothing
except for details from his journal written during a long
vacation trip abroad that lasted from June to September.
On this he accompanied his father, mother, and two oldest
sisters, who were all enclosed in the family carriage drawn
by local horses, usually four, but sometimes six or even
eight. France was under partial military occupation, and
Wellington, as well as Louis XVIII, was on view in Paris.
Note was taken of all objects of interest on the way, including geological exposures and a surprising abundance
of English people. A fortnight in Paris was devoted to
palaces, gardens, churches, museums, galleries, theatres,
Mass, opera, plays, and switchbacks, especially *Le Saut de
Niagara*, 'infinitely more rapid than any other in Paris, but
very delightful, not only to Parisians'. Apart from *Le Saut*,
Lyell seems to have derived most pleasure from Cuvier's
vast collection illustrating comparative anatomy—he did
not meet Cuvier on this occasion, for the great man happened to be in England. Lyell was also much impressed by
the numbers of students reading in the Bibliothèque du Roi
in happy contrast to the few he was accustomed to see in
the Bodleian.

Leaving Paris the party drove southeast by Fontainebleau, Auxerre, Dijon, Poligny, Morez, Geneva. Before

reaching Poligny Lyell's main interest was the succession
of rock exposures: Tertiary at Fontainebleau, then mostly
Chalk to Auxerre, followed by Jurassic to Dijon with a
midway outcrop of granite west of the Armançon. This
granite belongs to the extreme northern tip of the Central
Plateau. Of course of the four names employed above Lyell

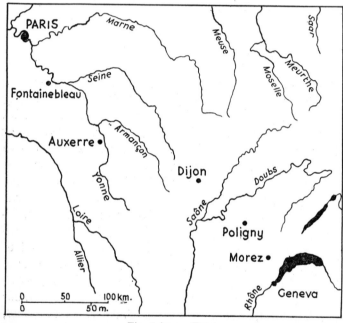

Fig. 5 Across France

only used Chalk and granite; but Tertiary and Jurassic
are justifiable present-day translations of what he says of the
two others. He undoubtedly recognized an age-sequence,
for he called the granite Primitive, which is relatively correct in this local setting, and he correlated the Jurassic encountered on its two sides because of abundant 'Ammonites,
some as large as the crown of my hat, some considerably
larger, with many gryphites and other shells'. Naturally

nothing that he has to say at this stage concerning well-trodden ground has contributed to the advancement of science; but it has a personal interest like the early words of a baby learning to speak.

After crossing the featureless Tertiaries of the Saône depression Lyell noted the horizontality of Jurassic limestone rising above Poligny. He had entered the Jura Mountains, but it so happened that folding was not very strikingly displayed along the route through Morez, and it seems to have attracted but little of his attention. On the other hand the trees and flowers of the roadside and the scenic glory of the Alps across Lake Geneva received proper recognition; while a couple of days in the town of Geneva gave time to note that 'the large spreading straw bonnets are very becoming to the women, and a pretty girl seems not such a rarity in a shop as in Paris'. It was on 1 July that the Lyell family entered Switzerland. Here they were to remain, travelling to and fro, until they crossed the Simplon into Italy on 15 August.

From Geneva the party made a digression into the Chamonix district, during which Lyell undertook two arduous days with a guide. Any attempt at stratigraphy was naturally hopeless, but there was plenty to see in the way of gorges, waterfalls, mud-laden torrents, avalanches, and above all glaciers, the last-named nearing the end of a minor period of advance. Lyell saw the Bossons glacier entering the Chamonix valley and in slow motion treading down 'the tallest pines with as much ease as an elephant would the herbage of a meadow'. In front had been planted a small wooden cross pathetically invoking divine intervention. Lyell fully realized what disaster might result if this glacier eventually blocked the Arve which flowed along the main valley down below. Only three weeks previously the Giétroz glacier, after damming the Drance de Bagnes above Martigny, had failed, thus releasing a torrent to sweep away villages. This disaster Lyell determined to investigate. Meanwhile he caught butterflies that he knew at best as rarities at home; and if he looked elsewhere he saw multitudes of English—a thousand by the aid of horse-transport had visited Chamonix the previous year. As for

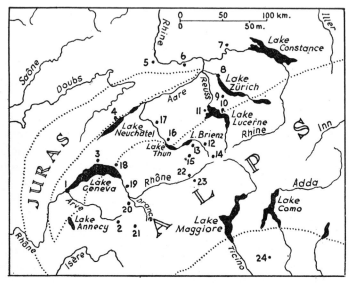

Fig. 6 Round about Switzerland

1. Geneva	7. Schaffhausen	13. Giessbach Falls	19. Bex
2. Chamonix	8. Zürich	14. Grimsel Hospice	20. Martigny
3. Lausanne	9. Zug	15. Grindelwald	21. St Bernard H.
4. Neuchâtel	10. Rigi	16. Thun	22. Brig
5. Basel	11. Lucerne	17. Berne	23. Simplon
6. Laufenburg	12. Meyringen	18. Vevey	24. Milan

the residents he learned there had been a recent bulge, as we call it today, resulting from Napoleon's policy of not conscripting married men to accompany him to Russia. Large spreading straw bonnets are not mentioned. Instead we learn that the people of the valley 'are in general fright-fully plain, owing chiefly to the goitres, to which the women are more liable than men'. After driving back to Geneva the party went by Lausanne to Neuchâtel, and thence to Basel. In this case some folds were recorded in the Juras, though rather quaintly: the strata, we are told, are 'much disturbed, but answering in general one way with the other in their inclination'. Pictures and fossils are seen at Basel; but the best sights lie farther up the Rhine: the rapids at Laufenburg and the great falls at Schaffhausen.

Turning from the German frontier the party then drove south through corn and poppy fields to Zürich, and so to Zug. Here young Lyell detached himself to visit an imposing landslip which twelve years previously had buried a whole village. As his guide pointed out, this recent fall stood in the midst of an earlier, more extensive slip; and yet a church and large inn had already been built upon its debris.

A climb up the Rigi was rewarded by the sight of its remarkable conglomerate cliffs, and by extensive views that open up in all directions. The inn at the top was over-full; and next morning before 3 a.m. 'nearly forty miserable half-dressed and shivering wretches were to be seen crowding round the crucifix on the highest point of the Righi-Culm'. Under the circumstances it was agreed 'that the view was less grand by sunrise than sunset'.

After the reunion of the family at Lucerne the carriage was dispatched by lowland routes to Thun, while a start was made by boat and mule or on foot to cross the Brünig and two Scheidegg passes. Young Lyell walked whenever possible and met much of interest on the way. Thus at Meyringen after the Brünig he braved heavy rain to see and hear a tributary of the Aare black with slate powder which a scorching sun had previously helped to prepare; and before his eyes the mud-stream constantly changed its direction, 'from the large mass of matter which was moving in its bed. . . . The rocks seemed actually to float in it, and a trifling depth of it was pushing heavy bodies along.'

Back with the family from Meyringen he also saw the

Giessbach Falls at Lake Brienz and the wonderful canyon upstream to the Fall of the Aare. From the latter he again went off on his own, anxious to visit the Rhône issuing from its parent glacier, and separated from the source of the Aare by the Grimsel Pass. At one point on the way he notes 'extraordinary large bare planks of granite rock above our track, the appearance of which I could not account for'. Lyell at the time had no inkling that there had been a Great Ice Age. His biographer Professor T. G. Bonney remarks of these exposures that they afford 'perhaps the finest examples of ice-worn rocks in Switzerland'. After sleeping at Grimsel Hospice Lyell made his way to the start of the Rhône and back to Meyringen; and then next day across the two Scheidegg passes to the Lauterbrunnen valley. In three successive days his walking in mountainous country has added up to 8 + 11 + 14 leagues, which can be reckoned good going; but when he boasted of it to a guide, he is put in his place with: 'Oui c'est assez pour un Monsieur.' 'A just reproof', Lyell acknowledged, for wherever the Monsieur went the peasant followed carrying the bag and 'without the same mental stimulus to assist him'.

At Grindelwald, between the Scheidegg passes, Lyell bought a few trifles from La belle Elizabeth to entitle him to add his name to the hundreds of English signatures already in her album. He was not disappointed, for he notes in his journal: She 'deserves, I think, her great fame for beauty'. Of more commonplace attractions he records the descent of a great avalanche from one ledge to another of the 'huge and tremendous precipice' of the Eiger.

From Thun the family reunited struck out by carriage for Berne in the heart of the Swiss Plain; and thence south-westwards they returned to Lake Geneva at Vevey. Then, hugging the shore by the Château de Clarens, 'immortalised' by Rousseau, and the Château de Chillon, 'which Lord Byron has made equally celebrated', they reached the

Rhône and proceeded to Bex. Here they traversed galleries that had been driven into the rock to gather brine that seeps out of Trias. They had, of course, no knowledge that the salt of Bex is of the same age as that of Cheshire.

Continuing up the Valais, they approached Martigny and met abundant evidence of the recent flood disaster of which we have already spoken. It had occurred on the 16th of June, and now on the 18th of August road and fields were still partly under water or hidden beneath sand. Of driftwood there was plenty. One tall pine with a diameter of eighteen inches lay there checked by a pollard poplar, around which it had wound itself, cracking in the process. At Martigny they found that the first storey of the post-house had been choked with debris, now thrown out into the court.

Lyell procured a mule and guide and pressed on up the devastated valley of the Drance for some twenty miles, experiencing a good deal of difficulty and even some slight danger due to broken or partially mended bridges. At last he found himself facing 'Mont Pleureur, a tremendous precipice, over the brow of which peeps the glacier of Getroz, which increased so much in the last severe winter, that it thrust over immense masses of ice. These falling with the snow in the spring, completely blocked up the narrow chasm into which the valley is here contracted. An immense lake was soon collected from the stoppage of so considerable a river as the Drance. Every exertion appears to have been made, and two thirds of the lake successfully drained out. It was the remaining third which had force to lay waste so much land'.

Owing to warnings only twenty-five people were killed on 16 June, and these mostly in Martigny which was thought to be beyond the danger zone. Apparently only one of the prearranged hilltop beacons was lighted; but it saved hundreds of lives.

After visiting the St Bernard Hospice and travelling to
Brig at the head of the Valais, the family climbed the
Simplon Pass behind eight horses. Great was their admiration for the road-work of Napoleon's engineers, towards
the maintenance of which they paid twenty-six shillings in
toll. Once well over the top they found that 'the difference
of the Italian side of the Alps is as remarkable as that of
the southern side of a garden wall'.

Leaving the Alps at Lake Maggiore the family drove
over a great stretch of alluvium deposited by tributaries of
the Po—Ticino, Adda, etc. They passed through Milan,
Brescia, Verona, Padua (Fig. 9); and then took boat to
Venice. Geology was forgotten with all solid rocks hidden
under foot; but art and human history, agriculture and fire-
flies were enough in themselves. Two nights were spent
at Venice, where naturally the bronze horses of Lysippus
were carefully examined. On return to Padua the drive
was continued over the same great plain by Ferrara to
Bologna.

Then by contrast came the crossing of the Apennines
to reach Florence, which brought to the carriage the rare
distinction of having four oxen hitched in front of its four
horses. Here solid rocks emerge from beneath alluvial
cover, and Lyell noted how each in turn according to its
particular nature influenced the character of the scenery.
Finally great comfort was found in 'Sneider's Hotel, which
is famed as being the first in Europe'. Next morning, a
begging procession was prefaced by 'a letter celebrating
both in verse and prose, both in English, Italian, and
French, the auspicious arrival of Sir Lyell and his illustrious family'. After dwelling upon the wealth and naval
power of England, the poet hoped 'to share in the fruits of
the unbounded generosity of the English'.

Here we must stop since Lyell's notebook with the rest
of his 1818 journal has been lost. As he spent much of his

life in comparable excursions, we shall have to be even briefer in subsequent notices; but this outing has been treated a little fully, not only as illustrating early stages in Lyell's education in the sculpture of landscape by erosion, but also as a sample of the wonderful post-Napoleonic resuscitation of the Grand Tour. About forty years later, in 1856, Thomas Cook, with the help of railways, was able widely to extend its clientele.

Of Lyell's doings in his last year at Oxford, 1819, we merely know that in March he became a fellow of both the Geological and the Linnean Societies of London, and that in December he took his B.A. with second class honours in Classics.

The same year, we may recall, Buckland was appointed full Professor of Geology. Noah's flood was lapping at his door, and his buoyant reaction may be gathered from the following quotation taken from his inaugural lecture: 'The grand fact of an universal deluge at no very remote period is proved on grounds so decisive and incontrovertible, that had we never heard of such an event from Scripture or any other Authority, Geology of itself must have called in the assistance of some such catastrophe to explain the phenomena of diluvial action.' Some twenty years were still to pass before he should reinterpret his universal deluge in terms of widespread glaciation.

Meanwhile let us look in at Cambridge for a moment, where something very remarkable had happened the year before Lyell graduated at Oxford, something that was to affect him quite considerably in common with all other geologists. In 1818 a popular don, Adam Sedgwick (1785-1873), with no claims to previous geological experience but with promises to leave no stone unturned if given the chance, was elected Woodwardian Professor of Geology. The strange experiment succeeded, for Sedgwick soon came to be recognized as England's leading field geologist—

though, as he told Lyell later, he wasted 1818 and 1819 through starting as a Wernerian rather than a Smithian stratigrapher.

1820-23 Mantell's Reptiles and Buckland's Reliquiae

After leaving Oxford Lyell was entered at Lincoln's Inn, and, living in London, studied law in a special pleader's office. His eyes troubled him, and he was recommended to stop reading for the present. So in the autumn of 1820 he joined his father in a second continental tour. We are told that there was 'no time to devote to geology, as they were busy seeing the towns, pictures and natural scenery'. They did not go beyond Rome because of disturbances farther south, which were likely soon to be aggravated by the arrival of 400,000 hated Austrians.

Next year,[1] 1821, Lyell attended Jameson's lectures in Edinburgh; and later, in October, called on Gideon Mantell (1790-1852), a distinguished Sussex geologist. This visit initiated a life-long friendship: thirty-seven of Lyell's published letters are addressed to Mantell.

The first meeting was unpremeditated. Lyell, riding alone, had visited his old school at Midhurst (Fig. 1), and then had spoken to some workmen in a neighbouring quarry. From them he learnt of a 'monstrous clever mon, as lived in Lewes, a doctor, who knowed all about them things, and got curiosities out of the chalk-pits to make physic with'. Lyell, having nothing special on hand, rode gently over the South Downs, some twenty-five miles, and at the close of the day presented himself at the doctor's doorstep. Common interest supplied sufficient introduction, and after drawers of fossils had been examined the two 'were in gossip until morning'. This incident is re-

[1] Lyell has mixed his dates in an account written to Miss Horner in 1832.

called in a letter which Mantell wrote twenty years later to Professor Silliman of Yale, New Haven, U.S.A., who was anxious to know what manner of man they were to expect, for Lyell was at that time soon to visit the United States. The following is the word-portrait supplied based on intercourse from 1821 to 1841:

> In person Mr. Lyell presents nothing remarkable, except a broad expanse of forehead. He is of a middle size, a decided Scottish physiognomy, small eyes, fine chin, and a rather proud or reserved expression of countenance. He is very absent, and a slow but profound thinker. . . . He always takes part in the discussions at the meetings of the Geological Society, but he has no faculty in speaking; there is hesitation in his manner, and his voice is neither powerful nor melodious, nor is his action at all imposing. As a popular lecturer he would stand no chance with Buckland or Sedgwick. . . . There is a hauteur or reserve about Mr. Lyell to strangers that prevents him being so popular among our society as he deserves to be. I believe him to have an excellent heart, and he is very kind and affectionate when his better feelings are called upon. I have had some reason to complain on points relating to authorship, but that, perhaps, is mere weakness of human nature. I am very much attached to him. I have only to regret that he has not that warmth of feeling which I had hoped to find in him, and which would have rendered him an invaluable friend to me. . . . Perhaps we Southrons are of more excitable stuff than the Northmen.

The first talk had lasted into the small hours; and after breakfast Lyell was round again to say goodbye. As he was heading for Brighton and thence along the coast to Bognor, Mantell mounted, and so to Ditchling where he showed his new friend the general features of the country, with which, quite understandably, he was enchanted.

Mantell at the time was on the eve of publishing his quarto volume on *The Fossils of the South Downs*, adorned with forty-two plates executed by his wife. The work appeared under the patronage of King George IV, with 130 advance subscribers including three earls and two bishops. Mantell was the son of a well-to-do shoemaker, reputedly descended from a companion of William the Conqueror. He himself was a kind-hearted surgeon and accoucheur, who seems to have bled his patients with almost equal zest whether rich or poor. In spite of this, by rationing himself to four hours sleep per diem, he found time to be an exceedingly keen geologist. Early in life he was encouraged by Parkinson, and later by the interest evinced by royalty and nobility in his discoveries of giant reptiles in the Weald formation. His genuine pleasure at securing royal patronage is amusing, for his journal for 14 November 1820 records his participation in the 'splendid illumination [that] took place this evening in honour of the acquittal of Her Majesty [Queen Caroline, whom the government at King George's behest had accused of adultery]. The Study was decorated with busts, statues and fossils, and looked very brilliant: the streets were thronged with spectators. At nine o'clock fire-works became very general, and the Market bell was rung for some time.'

The first three of Lyell's published letters to Mantell are dated February and April 1822, whereas Mantell's *Fossils of the South Downs* did not appear till May. In the first, Lyell gives an entertaining account of the Annual Dinner of the Geological Society. At it Buckland was called upon to explain the vast quantity of bones he had found in a hyena's den at Kirkdale, twenty-five miles E. of N. from York (Fig. 1). 'Buckland, in his usual style, enlarged on the marvel with such a strange mixture of the humorous and the serious, that we could none of us discern how far he believed himself what he said.' Lyell's two following letters record an advance into the Weald, which soon was sufficiently important for Mantell to write in June to the Geological Society indicating resultant correction in the stratigraphical data he had just published in his book.

Buckland's hyena cave, it may be noted, was splendidly produced in the *Philosophical Transactions*, 1822, and won for its author the Copley Medal, the highest award in the gift of the Royal Society. In 1823 it was republished, along with much additional matter, as the famous *Reliquiae Diluvianae*. Here we find a fascinating account of most of the

Fig. 7 Buckland entering Kirkdale Cavern. A caricature sketch by W. D. Conybeare.

known bone-caves of England, Wales, and Germany, some of the last-named visited in 1816 and 1822. Can one imagine a more striking appeal from past to present than is afforded by the Professor feeding bones of ox and sheep to a hyena that had visited Oxford in a travelling menagerie, and recovering from the keeper bony pellets of dung? Or can one resist the mathematical charm of a calculation which finds that, if two and a half bears die per annum in a cave, they will in a thousand years supply 5,000 cubic feet of bear-bone-meal, equal in bulk to that found at Kühloch?

The 'ever memorable' John Hunter, we are told, had somewhat carelessly assumed that the Kühloch deposit must
have taken many thousands of years to accumulate; but this
would be longer than the interval between Adam and Noah!
Joking apart, the *Reliquiae Diluvianae* is full of good matter,
and has served as a great stimulus to cave exploration. A
reader who is not too fastidious can still enjoy Buckland's
conception of many caves as relics of a pre-Diluvial landscape, like dug-outs of modern experience, which may be
the sole survivors of a pre-battle topography; but Noah's
flood has passed out of geological speculation and can no
longer be held responsible for the extinction of Messrs
Mammoth and Co. In addition, it is interesting to note
that Buckland's review of non-cave diluvium shows an
early knowledge of such matters as Norwegian erratics in
East Anglia and James Hall's 'flood' phenomena in
Scotland. Hall (1760-1832) was the famous experimenter,
who accepted his friend Hutton's interpretation of igneous
rocks, but resorted to inundations to explain scenery. It
was he who introduced the term crag and tail, with
Edinburgh Castle Rock as a typical crag sheltering the
Royal Mile to Holyrood as the associated tail.

To keep in touch with contemporary research in another
direction we may note that in 1822 Sedgwick started to
decipher 'Transitional' stratigraphy in the Lake District,
when to his delight he first encountered William Smith at
Kirkby Lonsdale (Fig. 1). He continued this research during the next three seasons; and it led in 1828 to an un-
fulfilled plan to produce with Conybeare a second part of
the *Outlines* to deal especially with pre-Old-Red-Sandstone
geology.

Chapter 5

Geologists in Paris

In 1823 Lyell and William Henry Fitton (1780-1861) were elected joint Secretaries of the Geological Society—Fitton, though a pupil of Jameson, was a staunch supporter of Hutton's igneous rocks and Smith's stratigraphy. As for Lyell's election, it shows that he was early accepted, scientifically and socially, by the aristocrats who at that time were largely responsible for the advancement of the science both at home and abroad.

In the early summer of the same year, 1823, Lyell was one of a party, including Buckland, which visited the Isle of Wight. Here he made some new observations, later quoted by Mantell in his *Geology* of the island, published in 1847. Then, on 22 June he left London, bound for France, where he remained till well into September. Most of this time he spent in Paris. 'As my object', he told Mantell, 'is principally to perfect myself in the language, I court everything which brings me in contact with Frenchmen'—in fact he would be happy to be the bearer of presents of books, specimens, or what not.

Lyell travelled 'with most excellent letters of introduction from Buckland, Greenough, Grey Bennett, Professor Brochart, Dr Fitton, Webbe and Lambert, Etc.—to Humboldt, Cuvier, Brongniart, Cordier, Duvan, Prévost, Lefroy, Royer, Etc.' His presents included copies of Buckland's *Reliquiae* and a selection of specimens from Scotland

and the Isle of Wight. We have already introduced Cuvier and Brongniart. Of the others the versatile Alexander von Humboldt (1769-1859) was reckoned in Europe to be the most famous of men apart from Napoleon. Though of the German nobility, he settled in Paris from 1808 to 1827 to secure co-operation in production of twenty volumes on his *Travels in the Equinoctial Regions of the New Continent*. His *Kosmos* was to follow considerably later, in part posthumously. His *Travel* volumes exercised much influence on geology through their descriptions of volcanoes and earthquakes, and the world-wide breadth of their treatment; and his *Personal Narrative* helped to persuade Darwin to go voyaging on the *Beagle*. Constant Prévost was much more of Lyell's own type. In two years' time, as one of the very rare Actualists of France, he was ready openly to attack Cuvier's Catastrophic theories. It will be noticed that there is no mention of Lamarck; but by 1823 the great author of the *Natural History of Invertebrate Animals* (1815-22) had already entered the ten years of blindness that, in 1829, led to a pauper's grave.

Our knowledge of Lyell's doings during his stay in Paris depends upon a dozen letters to his father. He was pleased to report that Humboldt and Duvan both claimed acquaintance with him as the son of one who had done good work on cryptogams. Apart from this recommendation, his letters of introduction assured him a hearty welcome in scientific circles. He found Baron Cuvier's weekly soirées a 'great treat', brightened by a stepdaughter 'of most engaging manners, and very clever, . . . she is pretty, and very lively'. He also attended free lectures on mining, geology, chemistry, and zoology at the Jardin du Roi, which had temporarily regained its title after ranking as Jardin des Plantes following the Revolution.

Politics figured prominently in the Lyell bulletins. Louis XVIII was in the hands of the Ultra-royalists, who started a war in Spain with the blessing of the Holy Alliance despite strong English opposition. Its object was the restoration of Ferdinand VII, deposed by Napoleon. This was achieved, though unfortunately with an accompanying treacherous massacre of Spaniard by Spaniard. An equally murderous war was proceeding in Greece, leading eventually to the liberation of that country. A fellow-collegian persuaded Lyell to subscribe two guineas towards its continuance; while another young Englishman he met was just off to join with Lord Byron.

Ultra-royalism, Lyell found, is linked with Roman Catholicism: 'The congregations are amazingly increased, chiefly because ministers and persons in power, forming the bulk of their aristocracy, have made church-going so fashionable, that it is becoming contrary to *bon ton* for your carriage not to be seen there.' Whereas 'some conscientiously religious Liberals abstain with their families altogether from church, because they have not courage enough to brave the imputation of being place-hunters'. Lyell instituted an arrestingly contrasted comparison: 'At our revolutionary period, the Court and the fashionable civilians were the sceptics, and often the open scoffers. The Puritans were then the church-goers and Liberals. The Republican leaders in England were able to acquire power to check the Crown by precisely the same hypocrisy by which the modern French Ultras acquire unlimited force for the prerogative.' All this seems fair comment; but there is considerable *naïveté* in Lyell's condemnation of the French Government for 'open compulsion. For instance, every student of medicine is compelled to produce a certificate of confession before he can take his degree'. After all, at Oxford, his own university, and also at Cambridge, no student could take his degree unless he professed himself an Anglican.

Another quotation from Lyell runs as follows: 'That the
E

royal prerogative is very undefined here, is, I think, proved by their establishing "monasteries" and "taking the veil", which is in general believed to be unlawful.' As regards the monasteries, he had heard Humboldt remark: 'We have made a calculation, and find that there exist already more religious houses in Paris than before the Revolution. . . . These houses do not *yet* contain so many *inmates*.' As regards taking the veil, we read in another letter that the Council of State has ruled that the King could authorize the practice 'without the Chamber repealing the existing laws against it. Cuvier, a Protestant, was President of the Council, and gave his vote "with the Ultras". Since this time the Protestants of Paris, who before looked up to him as a leader, have held him in abomination'. From the modern, as opposed to early nineteenth-century, English point of view, it may appear that Cuvier did no more in this matter than stand for religious liberty; but Humboldt's 1823 summing-up of Cuvier's conduct as a whole is very severe: 'Cuvier's situation', he says, 'was a proud one while he stood in the very foremost rank of men of science in France, but when he betrayed the weakness of coveting ribbons, crosses, titles, and Court favour, he fell down to the lowest among his new competitors.'

Another remark of Humboldt's is worth quoting as illustrating the continuity of French political life: 'Every other man one meets is either minister or ex-minister. So frequent have been the changes. They are scattered as thick as the leaves in Autumn, and before one set have time to rot away, they are covered by another, and another.' Ex-ministers, Lyell learned, have pensions, so long as they do not vote against the government.

Father Lyell, with his big family, was anxious to hear how the law of equal inheritance was faring. His son explained the qualification of *majorat*, or limited entail. As for the general result, some held that it had increased wealth, population, ease, and happiness; while others opposed any improvement that led to 'increase of population, which idea they have chiefly derived from mistaking Malthus'. All seemed to agree that equal inheritance increased the expectancy of marriage for young ladies, while decreasing the expectancy of life for old chateaux.

Lyell did not tell his father much of his definitely geological activities. He had a number of discussions with Humboldt, who was evidently glad to hear of how the science was developing in Britain. 'I have promised Humboldt', we read in one letter, 'to pass the afternoon to-day in his study. His new edition serves as a famous lesson to me, in the comparison of England and the Continent. There are few heroes who lose so little by being approached as Humboldt. Of Cuvier this cannot be said.' Lyell also undertook a few excursions, the two most important along with Prévost, with whom a return visit to England was planned for the next year. We find Lyell particularly interested in the freshwater Tertiaries of the Paris basin, for which he had been prepared by a Recent shell-marl dug at Kinnordy, and by some of the Tertiary formations of the Isle of Wight. In this connection he twice mentioned French 'millstone quarries which supply nearly all Europe and North America'. The millstones were roughened by the prominent oogonium ('fruit') of *Chara* (stonewort). Lyell also spent a couple of mornings with the young Baron de Férussac who 'has the finest collection by far of land and freshwater shells in the world'; and he fought 'hard with him for Buckland's notions of the Diluvial formation, in which Férussac is not orthodox'. This statement is specially interesting as showing that in 1823 Lyell was an adherent of Buckland. De Férussac's heresy restricted Noah's flood to such regions as had already been occupied by man. These did not, according to current opinion, include mammoth-infested Europe.

Lyell's eyes continued to trouble him during his stay in Paris and greatly restricted his reading, writing, and attendance at theatres. From Paris he returned to London via Holland.

Chapter 6

1824-1827

Home Geology and Lamarck

In the early summer of 1824 Lyell accompanied Prévost from London to Bristol and Land's End, coming back by the south coast to Hampshire. Lyell was greatly interested in the Transition rocks of the West, while Prévost was specially concerned with comparison of the Oolites of England with those of Normandy. It was a great year for Mary Anning at Lyme Regis, where first a Plesiosaurus with forty neck vertebrae (a swan has only twenty) was discovered, and then two 'magnificent' Ichthyosauri. The last of the three was obligingly found while Lyell and Prévost were in residence.

The latter part of the summer of 1824, together with the autumn, Lyell mostly devoted to Scottish geology. First he undertook a semi-pioneer exploration of a wide district about Kinnordy, extending from the Sidlaws across Strathmore into the Highlands as far as Mount Battock. To this we shall recur after noting a more linear excursion with Buckland from Kinnordy by Stonehaven, Aberdeen, Elgin, and Inverness to Brora; then back to Inverness and, after a diversion to Glen Roy, south by Blair Atholl, Glen Tilt, Perth, and Kinnordy to Edinburgh.

At Brora they recognized, or perhaps merely confirmed, the Oolitic age of the local coalfield. This information they passed on before long to Murchison, who after studying the exposures read a paper on the subject to the Geological Society in 1827.

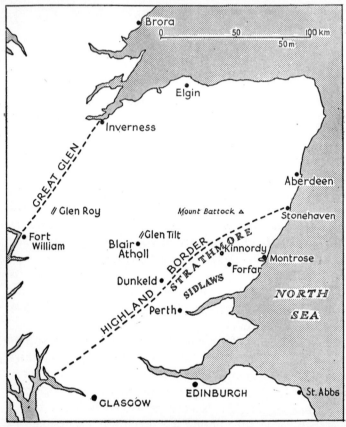

Fig. 8 Scotland

Roderick Impey Murchison (1782-1871) as a boy of seventeen carried the colours of his regiment during the retreat on Corunna. After Waterloo he married and was demobilized. His main interest for years was fox-hunting; but his wife aimed at something more intellectual. In 1823 she got her reward, for her husband, out shooting partridges with Humphry Davy, learned that it is possible to pursue philosophy without abandoning field sports—Davy

himself was a confirmed angler. So Murchison, after selling
his hunters, brought into his drawing-room for the purpose,
migrated to London, attended Davy's lectures at the Royal
Institution, and in 1824, the year we are now considering,
joined the Geological Society. It is pleasant to recall that
Murchison received his baptism in field geology the following year from the merry Buckland himself, when he
rode out with a party of Oxford students to listen en-
thralled while a landscape was geologically dissected.

To return to 1824. Buckland and Lyell found the Parallel
Roads of Glen Roy 'one of the grandest natural phenomena
in Great Britain' (Figs. 13, 15; Pl. 12). We shall hear
more about them presently in connection with Darwin
and Agassiz.

With Glen Tilt they were also 'much pleased', presumably because of the granite veins that had so delighted
Hutton.

Arrived at Edinburgh they were 'worked very hard in
the geology of the district', interlarded 'with breakfasts
and dinners without end', twice at Jameson's, etc., etc. They
then called on old Sir James Hall near St Abb's Head, and
had some 'great expeditions'. As usual Lyell in his des-
criptive letters included the ladies of the family: 'Lady
Helen Hall is daughter of the late Lord Selkirk; the two
unmarried daughters are very pleasant, one of them very
pretty.' When an end came to their happy visit Buckland
left for Alnwick Castle in Northumberland.

At two meetings of the Geological Society, 1824-5, Lyell
presented an interesting paper on a Recent freshwater limestone and marl dug at Bailie, five miles west-southwest of
Kinnordy. The deposit had yielded remains of stag, bull,
and wild boar; and Lyell recalled similar occurrences where
upright skeletons had been described with noses held erect.
He agreed that the animals had been mired, very likely
through venturing on treacherous ice. He listed the mol-

luscs of the marl, and supplied beautiful pictures by the younger Sowerby of the oogonia of *Chara*. Naturally he drew comparison with other Recent Marls near at hand and in Hampshire and with Tertiary limestones of France and Italy. As regards the pre-marl succession, he started with the Mount Battock granite, followed by gneiss, mica-slate, and greywacke; then Inferior Sandstone, 'in all parts interfered with by rocks of the Trap family'; and, above this, Old Red Sandstone. The last-named was overlain by vast deposits of moundy gravel which 'by Professor Buckland would be called diluvium'. Structurally Lyell recognized a pre-diluvial Montrose anticline running southwest and separated from the Highlands by a Strathmore syncline. None of the pre-marl formations yielded him fossils, so it is little surprising that his succession has a distinctly Wernerian flavour. Still one feels that he might have had second thoughts about the Mount Battock granite after seeing Glen Tilt. His Inferior Sandstone with its interfering traps is now known to be the lower part of the local development of Old Red Sandstone.

Another paper was published in the *Edinburgh Journal of Science*, 1825. In it he (along with Buckland and later W. J. Judd, but not, later still, D. A. Allan) very understandably mistook a pre-Old-Red Highland-Border serpentine, north of Kinnordy, for a dyke intruded into Old Red Sandstone.

Lyell's sister-in-law, Katherine M. (sister of his wife Mary and married to his soldier brother Henry), tells us that by this time his eyes had grown stronger, and that at his father's request he resumed his study of the law. So in 1825 he was called to the bar, and went on the Western Circuit for the next two years.

A letter to Mantell dated 1825 affords an interesting sidelight. 'Your great valley', it says, meaning the Weald surrounded by the chalk escarpment, 'is not a valley of denudation. I do not agree with Buckland that much chalk has been carried away between the north and south downs'. Instead Lyell regards the 'opening of some miles' as largely a tensional effect accompanying the arching of the district. He has indeed a great deal to learn!

Another point we may note is that Lyell in 1825 was joined by George Poulett Scrope (1797-1876) in the Secretaryship of the Geological Society. Both retired the next year, to be followed by Broderip and Murchison. Scrope in 1825 published *Considerations on Volcanoes*, a work that shows wide field acquaintance with the subject, combined with much rather ill-advised speculation. We also learn that Lyell's sister, Marianne, now co-operates in his still lively interest in insects; while he himself has started to contribute to the *Quarterly Review*, earning money thereby.

In 1826 Lyell read a couple of papers at the Geological Society on Tertiary exposures of the Hampshire coast. An interesting sentence may be quoted: 'The size of the valleys is in general in proportion to that of the streams flowing in them, and their excavation appears referable for the most part, if not entirely, to the long continued agency of these streams.' In this instance Lyell does not invoke the aid of sea erosion, but gives instead a restatement of what long afterwards the great American geographer, W. M. Davis, called the Playfair Law of river development— actually Playfair inherited it from Hutton. Readers must judge for themselves whether or no this so-called law is preferable to Buckland's counterclaim, namely that valleys, even valleys obviously produced by water erosion, determine the size of occupying rivers, not *vice versa*. Buckland, of course, admitted that rivers can be seen to erode, but only, he maintained, on a trifling scale. For him valleys of erosion must be attributed to transient deluges. He revolted against admitting the efficacy of Huttonian time.

Lyell's connection with the *Quarterly Review* brought

him into pleasurable contact with the new editor, John Lockhart, and his father-in-law, Sir Walter Scott; while a week at Cambridge introduced him to John Stevens Henslow, Professor of Botany, who was destined soon to exercise great influence on the career of young Darwin. Other events of 1826 were election to the Royal Society— an easier matter then than now—and the family's departure from Bartley Lodge to reside henceforward at Kinnordy, which brought Lyell in retrospect to realize that after all he had had a happy childhood.

Lyell on circuit, 1827, received from Mantell a copy of 'Lamarck'. This may have meant Lamarck's *Philosophie Zoologique* (1809), or perhaps his *Histoire naturelle des Animaux sans Vertèbres* (1815-22), which its author completed with a daughter's help after the onset of blindness. It is suggestive to find that three partial English translations of the latter appeared between 1822 and 1825, and that either in 1826 or 1827 Darwin in Edinburgh 'listened in silent astonishment' to a lecturer, Dr R. E. Grant, who 'burst forth in high admiration of Lamarck and his views on evolution'. (Grant in the *Edinburgh Philosophical Journal*, 1826, vol. 14, p. 283, clearly adopts the view that species are descended from other species.)

'I devoured Lamarck *en voyage*', Lyell adds in thanking Mantell, 'his theories delighted me more than any novel I ever read. . . . But though I admire even his flights, and feel none of the *odium theologicum* which some modern writers in this country have visited him with, I confess I read him rather as I hear an advocate on the wrong side, to know what can be made of the case in good hands. I am glad he has been courageous enough and logical enough to admit that his argument, if pushed as far as it must go, if worth anything, would prove that men may have come from the Ourang Outang.'

For himself, Lyell recognized exits from the palaeontological succession; but entries he attributed to imperfection of the geological record. 'If I am asked why in coal there are no quadrupeds? I answer, why are there none . . . in the plastic clay or lignite formation' of the Tertiaries. Today this one-sided theory of elimination seems an extraordinary hypothesis; but Lyell boldly states: 'I am going to write in confirmation of ancient causes having been the same as modern, and to show that those plants and animals which we know are becoming preserved now are the same as were formerly.' We learn later from the preface to Volume 3 of the *Principles*, when it appeared in 1833, that: 'The original MS. of the "Principles of Geology" was delivered to the publisher at the close of the year 1827'—but important changes were made in ensuing years.

Chapter 7

Auvergne – Sicily – Scrope –
Olot – Deshayes

1827-9 Auvergne to Sicily

In 1827 Lyell read a short paper on elephant bones found near Salisbury (Fig. 1), but much more important is his review, or perhaps one should say rewriting, forty-seven pages long, of Scrope's recently published *Geology of Central France* (Fig. 9). This last is a remarkable book, the result of six months' intensive field study and sketching. It was written in 1822, but its appearance was delayed owing to the 'natural unwillingness of publishers to undertake scientific works with expensive plates'—in this case eighteen panoramas, two of them six feet long illustrating Auvergne, Velay (Haute-Loire) and Vivarais, the most geologically picturesque district in the world. Scrope makes no claim to originality, but insists on independence. He was led to the region by current widespread knowledge that various authors, mainly French but including Leopold von Buch, had described a time-succession from Primitive rocks, largely granite, and Secondaries, largely Jurassic limestone, to Tertiaries, both freshwater sediments and a varied assemblage of volcanics; and that some had also attributed wonderful effects to river erosion. Scrope determined to be 'wholly uninfluenced by any previously formed opinions on the district . . . having laid down and adhered to a resolution not to open any author who had written on the subject

. . . the following Memoir . . . pretends to little other merit than that of independence and fidelity'. Keeping much closer to observation than in his *Considerations,* and depending largely upon his artistic skill, Scrope made a great success of this strangely exclusive contribution to science! He was deeply impressed by the manner in which the interaction of vulcanicity and erosion had incidentally furnished proofs that a great deal of the denudation of the district had been spread over a lengthy period during which it had been concentrated along river channels; so that it had neither the instantaneity nor the boundlessness that are postulated for a deluge. Thus, many successive lavas have been poured out upon successively lower slopes of erosion; and those that have flowed into pre-existent valleys from incoherent ash-cones at higher level have commonly been deeply dissected by restored river activity, while the much weaker cones have escaped almost unscathed. He concludes with the declaration:

The leading idea which is present in all our researches, and which accompanies every fresh observation, the sound which to the ear of the student of Nature seems continually echoed from every part of her works, is — 'Time! — Time! — Time!'

Lyell's comment is:

The principal question at issue between Mr. Scrope and several other English geologists who have visited Auvergne, relates to the formation of valleys; and whatever may be the merits of the rival theories, we consider this work the most able which has appeared since Playfair's 'Illustrations of the Huttonian Theory', in support of the opinion that valleys, which decidedly owe their form to the agency of water, have not been shaped out by one sudden and violent inundation, but progressively by the action of rivers, or of such floods as may occur in the ordinary course of nature. . . . The interior of France is so peculiarly adapted for the decision of this question, that we have great reason to regret the death of Professor Playfair so soon after his visit [1816] to Auvergne, and before he had published his observations on the subject.

Further on Lyell makes a strong appeal for religious toleration to be extended to all seeking to understand the handiwork of the 'Author of Nature'.

It appears from Lyell's letters of this time that sister Caroline as well as Marianne was insect-minded. He assured them that great finds might be expected at Kinnordy, since the Scottish fauna was much less explored than the English. His desultory law practice cost his father a little money, but Lyell was loth to abandon it altogether, for it provided an 'excuse deemed valid for declining unprofitable parties, or refereeships of papers or secretaryships, etc.' Still, in 1828 he acceded to his father's advice, and henceforward devoted himself wholly to authorship, predominantly, but by no means exclusively, geological.

Lyell celebrated his new start by an excursion abroad lasting from May 1828 to February 1829. The first six months were spent in company with Mr and Mrs Murchison surveying French and Italian geology from Auvergne to Padua (Fig. 9). They met in Paris, where Lyell was delighted to renew acquaintanceships, especially with Prévost—Humboldt had returned to Berlin in 1827.

From Paris the Murchisons and Lyell drove in a hired carriage or rode on horseback from place to place. Mrs Murchison had a Swiss maid, while Lyell, to begin with, was shadowed, at his anxious father's request, by his well-trained clerk, Hall by name, to treat his eyes in case of need. The clerk travelled independently and collected insects for Lyell's sisters, and plants, geologically sited, for William Hooker. The eyes got stronger and stronger.

Lyell, like all others, fell for Mrs Murchison. 'She is very diligent, sketching, labelling specimens, and making out shells, in which last she is an invaluable assistant. She is so much interested in the affair, as to be always desirous

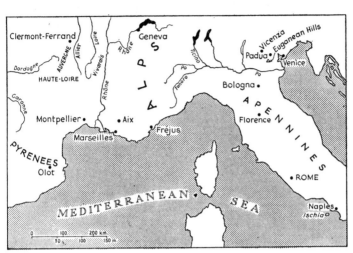

Fig. 9 Auvergne to Naples

of keeping out of the way when she would interfere with the work.' This last characteristic is illustrated in an account of a five-day excursion made shortly afterwards from Clermont-Ferrand. The first day 'Mrs Murchison accompanied us, and then returned to Clermont, where she employed herself during our absence in making panoramic sketches, receiving several of the gentry and professors, to whom we had letters, in the neighbourhood, and collecting plants and shells, etc., while Murchison and I, with my man, went on in a *patache*, a one-horse machine on springs'.

As for Murchison, we hear that he 'certainly keeps it up with more energy than anyone I ever travelled with, for Buckland, though he worked as hard, always flew too fast to make sure of anything'. Sometimes, however, Murchison approached, or passed, the limit of endurance. 'One day,' says Lyell, 'we rode fifty-five miles, which I shall take care shall be the last experiment of that kind, as even the old Leicestershire fox-hunter was nearly done up with it.' Moreover the heat of August did not suit him, and we find that he collapsed at Fréjus, overcome by malaria, so that for the time being he could not 'take the field again. But we have been hard at work in writing, from our materials, a paper on the excavation of valleys, which is at last finished, and after two evenings' infliction, is intended to reform the Geological Society, and afterwards the world, on this hitherto-not-in-the-least-degree-understood subject. Besides this mighty operation, we have performed two jaunts with Mrs Murchison, each at half-past four in the morning, to see certain deposits of fossil shells and collecting these, with which she has been much pleased; . . . Our descent upon these hot latitudes, has restored her health and spirits, which had failed sadly. Her lord has a little too much of . . . "the keep-moving, go-it-if-it-kills-you" system, and I had to fight sometimes for the sake of geology, as his wife had for her strength, to make him proceed with somewhat less precipitation.'

A most amazing fact we learn about Murchison from one of Lyell's letters home, namely his dependence on drugs: 'On one occasion', Lyell writes, 'we were on an expedition together, and as a stronger dose was necessary than he had with him, I was not a little alarmed at finding there was no pharmacy in the place, but at last went to a nunnery, where Mlle. La Supérieure sold all medicines without profit—positively a young, clever, and rather good-looking lady, who hoped my friend would think better of it, as the quantity would kill six Frenchmen.' The drug is not named, but what an advertisement it might have received, considering the extraordinary output of this geological superman, continuing into his eightieth year when he dictated from his death-bed his last Presidential Address! One recalls George II's exclamation, when told that Wolfe was mad: 'I wish he would bite my other generals!'

Plates 6 and 7   Valleys eroded in Auvergne lavas.

Plate 8 Olot, drawn by Lyell.

Plate 9 Elevated Pleistocene shell-bed near Palermo, Sicily.

In relation to volcanics and erosion Lyell and Murchison's observations agree in character with those of Scrope. The newcomers, however, had covered a wider area and given much more attention to the freshwater sediments. Like Scrope they seem to have had little acquaintance with what had already been accomplished by French naturalists. They do, however, mention 'Desmarest's accurate map', and they single out Counts de Serres and Montlosier as living local authorities, the latter, however, now more concerned 'with a book against the Jesuits, a more popular subject in France at present than geology'. At Aix a laminated bed in the Tertiary marl had recently been discovered, full of perfectly preserved insects. 'Until we came all had gone to M. de Serres of Montpellier. He has made out fifty genera. . . . Murchison kept saying, when we were hunting about the quarries, and getting them from the man, "How I wish your sisters were here, they would enjoy the chase, and then we might be at work on the geology".'

The last combined attack was directed in September against the volcanic districts of Vicenza and the Euganean Hills, forty miles west of Venice, 'just Auvergne over again'. Before parting, Murchison urged Lyell to hurry south if he wished to publish his *Principles of Geology* by November 1829: 'Sicily', he said, 'is for your views the great end: there are the most modern analogies, volcanic, marine, elevatory, subsiding, etc. I know the island as a soldier, and if you make straight for Etna, will just time it right for work, for the season will be exactly suitable.'

We must pass quickly over Lyell's solo trip to Etna and back, which exceeded his 'warmest expectations in the way of modern analogies'. He spent six weeks in Sicily including the whole of December. This was probably later than Murchison had advised, but Lyell was blessed with unseasonably good weather and worked very hard. Billeting conditions were trying due to the increasing poverty of the

F

inhabitants southward from Rome. He took copious notes and specimens, and was greatly helped by determinations of his fossils by Italian experts. 'I am beginning', he wrote to Murchison from Naples on the return journey, 'I am beginning to be able, when I see large collections, to distinguish between any marked difference in the proportion of lost species and genera.' This remark illustrates the basis for his division of the Tertiary into systems, which he was soon publicly to advocate (p. 91). On the physical side he was delighted to be able to confirm that the celebrated Temple of Jupiter Serapis near Naples (destined to figure as frontispiece of his *Principles*, see our Pl. 10) does indeed provide evidence of subsidence and re-elevation in the form of holes bored by the marine lammellibranch, *Lithodomus*. The movement in each case exceeds twenty feet and must have been accomplished since early Christian days. Testimony of much bigger displacements, still dating from what are, geologically speaking, very recent times, he found at Ischia at 2,600 feet and at Etna at 3,800 feet, where many sea-shells of living species occur in sediments interbedded with lavas.

Lyell confides to Murchison that he wants his forthcoming book, 'in part written, and all planned', to pay the *additional* costs of his hobby, so that he can devote himself wholly to geology without feeling selfish. He considers that: 'This year we have by our joint tour fathomed the depth and ascertained the shallowness of the geologists of France and Italy as to their original observations.' But what of the Germans? 'Their language must be learnt; the places to which their memoirs relate, visited; and then you may see, as I may, to what extent we may indulge dreams of eminence, at least as original observers.' The principles which he proposes to elaborate in his forthcoming book 'are neither more nor less than that *no causes whatever* have from the earliest time to which we can look back, to the present, ever acted, but those *now acting'*.

Lyell soon heard with pleasure that Murchison, at two successive meetings of the Geological Society, had already presented their joint paper: 'On the Excavation of Valleys, as illustrated by the Volcanic rocks of Central France'. In it the authors refer 'especially to the works of M. de Montlosier (1788) and the illustrations of that district recently published by Mr. Scrope'; and also, as regards the efficacy of river erosion in general, to the writings of Horace Bénédict de Saussure (1786) and Playfair. Fortunately English readers can nowadays supplement these acknowledgments by turning to Archibald Geikie's *Founders of Geology*, which enables us to share in J. E. Guettard's pleasure in his discovery of the volcanoes concerned and in his realization of the importance of subaerial denudation. We can also appreciate Desmarest's grand development of Guettard's beginnings, his unravelling of the interplay of lava accumulation and river erosion, and his Actualistic inference 'that Nature had followed the same order of procedure in the most remote ages as in the most recent times'. According to Geikie, Desmarest's final memoir was laid before the Academy in 1775, published in abstract in 1779 and fully in 1806. Hutton's *Theory of the Earth* first appeared, it will be remembered, in 1788, the same year as Montlosier's memoir on Auvergne.

Lyell and Murchison, like Scrope, make no claim to originality of ideas, merely hoping that 'every additional fact and argument bearing on the subject will be of interest'. Their paper is a well documented guide-book to a supremely important district. Lyell is able to tell sister Marianne: 'My letters from geological friends are very satisfactory, as to the unusual interest excited in the Geological Society by our paper on the excavation of valleys in Auvergne. Seventy persons were present the second evening, and a warm debate. Buckland and Greenough furious, *contra*

Scrope, Sedgwick, and Warburton, supporting us. These were the first two nights in our new *magnificent* apartments in Somerset House.'

Naturally Lyell thought that Murchison, like himself, had definitely joined the Uniformitarian School. Possibly he had while the two were together in Auvergne; but once Murchison got back to England and talked things over with his friends, including Adam Sedgwick, who at that time was ranked by him and many others with his name-sake as the First of Men, he seems to have felt that he had gone too far. Sedgwick's attitude is beyond doubt, since it is stated in his 1830 Presidential Address to the Geological Society. He accepted the deep gorges of Auvergne as 'ex-cavated solely by the long continued attrition of the rivers which flow through them', but there are other valleys, 'for instance, the dry combes and valleys of the chalk, which appear to have been swept out by one flood of retiring waters during some period of elevation'.

That Murchison henceforward remained a Catastrophist is clear from the following anecdote concerning the publica-tion in 1885 of Geikie's *Scenery of Scotland*: 'The volume', Geikie says, 'was dedicated to Murchison, to whose friend-ship I owed so much. Yet its main thesis was in such direct antagonism with his well-known cataclysmic opinions that I was prepared for some protest on his part. But he ac-cepted the compliment without demur.'

Of other matters we need only mention Lyell's keen interest in the travertines and the marine Younger Ter-tiaries and early Quaternaries of Italy. He added greatly to his store of shells from the latter by collection, purchase, exchange, and gift. He discussed geology with every authority along his route. Early in February 1829 he crossed the Alps by Mont Cenis to call on the botanist Augustin Pyrame de Candolle at Geneva. De Candolle asked kindly after father Lyell and gave the son for himself 'his splendid essay on Geographical Botany, the most beautiful generalisation of a multitude of facts which I think was ever produced in natural history'.

A few days in Paris allowed Lyell to enjoy a lecture by Prévost 'on diluvium and caves, a good logical refutation of the diluvian humbug'. Much more important, they enabled Lyell to arrange 'a regular correspondence with Deshayes, now by far the principal conchologist in fossils', in fact 'the Cuvier of Tertiary shells'. Gérard Paul Deshayes (1795-1875) at this time found it very difficult to make a living. The public thought of little but politics and romances. Politics were indeed tumultuous. Charles X had succeeded to the throne in 1824 on the death of his brother Louis XVIII, and now faced a revolutionary close to his reign. Cuvier, it is true, could still mount a 'famous soirée', and could still publish profusely at a profit, 'without appearing to give himself the least trouble', but no other naturalist in Paris 'could persuade a librarian to publish one volume for nothing'. Even Cuvier could talk to Lyell only of 'the Catholic question, our [British] corporation rights, etc.', and nothing of geology.

Lyell helped Deshayes by purchasing his account of the shells of the Paris Basin so far as this had appeared. He also bought a set of named specimens for Mantell's museum, to which he added a gift from Cuvier of duplicate bonecasts. The co-operation with Deshayes, thus begun, soon proved immensely profitable in putting on a firm basis the division of the Tertiary epoch at which Lyell had already been aiming. Karl von Zittel, in commenting upon the partnership, remarks: 'It is difficult to tell in how far Lyell was the originator of the researches so brilliantly carried out by Deshayes; the distinguished British geologist had certainly devoted special attention to the Tertiary Molluscan faunas during his early journeys in Italy.' Lyell's own view was that his share in the research was important and complementary. We shall return to this point when we tell of his visit to Paris next year, 1830. Meanwhile we may note a further point made by Zittel, namely that his own distinguished master at Heidelberg, Professor H. G. Bronn, had, quite independently, studied the problem in Italy, and had arrived at the same general conclusions. Bronn's results were published in 1831, and to a considerable extent anticipated those set out by Lyell and Deshayes in the third volume of the *Principles*, 1833. (A reader will find supplementary discussion by Fitton in the *Edinburgh Review* for 1839; see also the present volume, p. 82.)

Before leaving Paris Lyell heard with regret that Buckland had signed an Oxford petition against Catholic emancipation. (Sedgwick vigorously, but unsuccessfully opposed a similar petition from Cambridge.) Mrs Buckland attributed her husband's action to what he had seen in Sicily; and Murchison, in passing on the information, hoped that Lyell's sojourn in that distressful island had not driven him also to intolerance. Lyell for his part thought it 'no small want of logic to confound the emancipation question with the state of Spain and Sicily. Besides, if fanaticism were to be the measure of disability, I fancy that no small part of our sectarians and even more orthodox saints would be entitled to their share.' The University petitions did not prevent Wellington's government from reluctantly piloting the Catholic Emancipation Bill through parliament the next April. A similar measure, covering non-conformists, had been passed the previous year. The emancipation thus achieved concerned matters national and municipal. The two ancient Universities were able to maintain their religious tests for graduation until 1871.

After return to London in February 1829 Lyell joined Murchison in presenting papers at the Geological Society on the Tertiary lake-deposits at Cantal and Aix (Fig. 9). The insect bed is dealt with by John Curtis, an expert who often exchanged modern specimens with Lyell's sisters.

Lyell, however, found more cause for excitement in meeting an onslaught upon his and Murchison's previous paper on river erosion in Auvergne. The enemy was led by Conybeare, with Buckland and Greenough in support. Conybeare took as his text the phenomena of the Thames drainage basin and, one must confess, he posed some puzzles which his opponents were not in a position satisfactorily to solve, such as: the way in which northern (we now say glacial) drift has extended into the basin; the manner in which streams have passed through escarpments; and the origin of the dry valleys of the chalk. Sedgwick in the Chair decided that we must 'doubt and not dogmatise', but all the same he was roused to deliver 'such a broadside at the finale . . . as was enough to sink the "Reliquiae Diluvianae" for ever'. Like Lyell, Sedgwick had changed his mind: in 1825 he had been prepared to defend Buckland's Noah's flood.

1829-30 Scrope – Olot – Deshayes

Lyell spent the summer of 1829 at Kinnordy, though keeping in touch by letter with Sedgwick and Murchison in their current attack upon the Tertiaries of Switzerland and Italy. By the end of the year the first volume of his *Principles of Geology* was in the press.

The first half of 1830 was largely occupied in correcting proofs. When this was completed we find Lyell writing a very informative letter to Scrope, dated 14 June. Scrope by this time had set aside geology for politics; but all the same he was selected by the *Quarterly Review* to deal with the forthcoming *Principles*. This choice, we learn, was made without any prompting from Lyell. Not unnaturally, Scrope asked his friend for clarification on certain points. Lyell in reply explains that one main aim has been to 'free the science from Moses'. In this matter, he thinks, 'Prévost has done a little but is a diluvialist, a rare thing in France'. 'Von Hoff', Lyell continues, 'has assisted me most, and you should compliment him for the German plodding perseverance with which he has filled two volumes with facts like tables of statistics; but he helped me not to my scientific views of causes.' Lyell was hampered in reading von Hoff owing to his ignorance of the German language; but his assessment is confirmed by Zittel. Von Hoff's first two volumes appeared in 1822 and 1824, and were valuable, critical compilations from existing literature—von Hoff had not the means to travel. Both dealt with changes that had occurred during historic times: the first volume in relation to the distribution of land and sea; the second in regard to the activity of volcanoes and earthquakes. The third volume appeared ten years later, and clearly shows, according to Zittel, the influence of Lyell's first volume, which by this time had appeared. In it 'Von Hoff discusses the causes of the degradation of land'.

Another interesting feature of Lyell's letter to Scrope is an explanation that he gives for saying with Hutton: there are 'no signs of a beginning, no prospect of an end'. 'There is no harm', he says to his reviewer, 'in your attacking me, provided you point out that it is the proof I deny, not the probability of a beginning.' One feels that for Lyell both beginning and end lay beyond the scope of geology.

Before the end of June, Lyell set out for the Pyrenees and Spain. He had as companion Commander Cooke R.N., a very agreeable naturalist and linguist, but one with distracting interests. These led to a detour to see the standing stones of Carnac, a suggestion to collect butterflies on the slopes of the Pyrenees, a weakness for pine forests and even an occasional desire to take a day off. In spite of these worries Lyell saw a lot of the French side of the Pyrenees and managed a dash into the northeastern corner of Spain to examine prehistoric volcanoes at Olot (Fig. 9; Pl. 8). He emerged from this rush on 7 August to find that a great revolution had occurred.

Actually it was the 1830 Revolution of the 'July days'. Paris had risen largely because of Charles X's appointment in 1829 of ministers distasteful to the majority of deputies. On 7 August the rump of the Chamber deposed Charles, and, to avoid intervention by the Holy Alliance, declared his cousin Louis-Philippe, formerly Duc d'Orléans, king in his stead. The way had been prepared: Thiers had proclaimed that the duke was 'a prince devoted to the Principles of the Revolution', one who had 'carried the tricolour under fire', and who could be trusted to be a 'citizen king'; while Lafayette had publicly embraced him at the Hôtel-de-Ville, the headquarters of the Republican party.

By October 1830 Lyell had worked his way to Paris. There he was disappointed to find all the scientists still talking politics instead of discussing his book. Prévost had just been dining with the Citizen King, on whom he had called in the uniform of a private of the National Guard to present an address from the Geological Society. He had 'made', says Lyell, 'little progress even in reading my book, which ere this he was to have half translated'. Even apart from politics, Prévost had found it difficult to puzzle out the meaning of some of the long sentences—and no wonder.

Poor Deshayes had not named Lyell's shells from Sicily. This was only indirectly due to the revolution. There was now so little demand for scientific publication that Deshayes must work for anyone willing to pay for anything; and this had left no time for making determinations without payment. Lyell had not fully realized how difficult life had become, and had not previously dared to offer a fee. Now he 'came to an agreement to take him off all other work in order to give me [Lyell] a private course of fossil

conchology, in which he is to give me all his time for a
month, towards the zoological part of Vol. 2, also to give
me two months' additional work when I am gone with the
results derivable from his and others' great collections in
Paris.' The intention of the latter part of this agreement
was to supply long fossil lists for Lyell to publish, with
acknowledgment, in advance of Deshayes' intended publication 'in a Manual of Conchology a year and a half since'.

Lyell's outlook on this transaction is clearly stated: 'I
shall thus be giving the subject a decided push, by render-
ing the greater wealth of the French collectors available in
illustrating the greater experience of the English geologists in actual observation, for here they sit still, and buy
shells, and work indoors, as much as we travel.'

On arrival in London in December, Lyell found his book
a popular success, which bade fair to 'earning a small but
honourable independence, if [he] labours as hard for the
next ten years as during the last three'. Scrope, by the
way, was rewarded with £100 from Lyell's publisher for
his review in the *Quarterly*, a very able *and* independent
production.

Chapter 8

1830-1833

Principles of Geology

1830 Volume 1

The first volume of Lyell's *Principles of Geology: being an attempt to explain the former changes of the Earth's surface by reference to causes now in operation* was published in 1830. Its frontispiece pictures the Temple of Jupiter Serapis, near Naples, to illustrate recent down and up movement of the earth's crust (Pl. 10). A geologically preferable drawing is substituted in the third edition, 1834.

Lyell appeals in Chapter 1 for the divorce of geology and cosmogony, just as history is divorced from theories of the creation of mankind. He then traces the development of the science in Chapters 2 to 4, since splendidly expanded by Geikie in his *Founders of Geology* and Zittel in his *History* of the same. Lyell starts with ancient cosmogonies of India, Egypt, and Greece, and ends approximately with the birth of the Geological Society of London, 1807. Some of the earliest accounts postulate long periods of alternate creation and destruction. According to Lyell these probably grew round traditions of disaster due to floods or volcanoes, supported by such marvels as fossils embedded in solid rock.

Passing to post-classical time, Lyell tells in detail of geological speculation, sadly hampered, first by Mohammedan orthodoxy, and later, in Europe, by Christian acceptance of the Mosaic record. One reads of Omar, in the earlier period, having to recant, thus leaving by the same door as in he came; and of Buffon, as late as 1751, called upon by the Faculty of Theology in Paris to renounce in print as impious his view: 'that the present mountains and valleys of the earth are due to secondary causes, and that the same causes will in time destroy all the continents, hills and valleys, and reproduce others like them.'

Lyell's familiarity with Italian and other literature concerning long-continued gropings after geological truths fills readers with admiration, increased by his acknowledgment of help from previous authors. Among such he cites the Hanoverian Rudolf Erik Raspe, 1763, with his review of the systems of Hooke, Ray, Moro, Buffon, and others, and the French Cuvier in his *éloges* on Pallas, Werner, and Desmarest.

Lyell's own *Principles* are for many of us a natural development of Hutton's *Theory of the Earth* (1788, 1795) as clarified in Playfair's delightful *Illustrations* (1802); and Fitton in the *Edinburgh Review* for 1839 urged him in friendly fashion to emphasize this fact more clearly in subsequent editions. Fitton's long article, which did not appear until after the publication of Lyell's *Elements*, to be noted later, is of great historical interest, especially owing to his exceptional acquaintance with current literature abroad, wherein scarcely any acknowledgment is to be found of Hutton's achievements, probably in many cases only known by hearsay. As for Lyell, he never was given to over-generous appreciation of work by others; but his record in regard to Hutton seems, by present-day standards, quite creditable. For instance, he prefaces Volume 1 with a long quotation:

Amid all the revolutions of the globe the economy of Nature has been uniform, and her laws are the only thing that have resisted the general movement. The rivers and the rocks, the seas and the continents have been changed in all their parts; but the laws which direct those changes, and the rules to which they are subject, have remained invariably the same. (Playfair, *Illustrations of the Huttonian theory*, § 374.)

Also in Chapter 4 he devotes five appreciative pages, as well as many subsequent references, to Hutton's work. (Here in passing, one criticism may be offered. Lyell was mistaken in thinking that Hutton pictured new continents as 'upheaved by violent and paroxysmal convulsions', different in degree from what has been happening, bit by bit, in some place or another, during human history. Playfair does indeed, in his *Illustrations*, use the words: 'violent', 'great convulsions', 'torn asunder and moved angularly', 'incredible energy', but just such phrases are employed by Lyell himself in relation to modern earthquakes.) Finally, Lyell knew, much more clearly than Hutton, that many of the latter's conclusions regarding erosion, deposition, time, ancient volcanoes, earth movement, etc., had been anticipated by some one observer or another. It may be added that it is always difficult to assess Hutton's undoubtedly great originality, because he seldom discusses the ideas of a forerunner or contemporary unless he thinks he has a correction to offer. Lyell has been more accommodating.

Lyell naturally knew infinitely more than Hutton about many aspects of his subject. He has said himself: it is 'certain that to travel is of threefold importance to those who desire to originate just and comprehensive views concerning the structure of this globe'. Travelling in Lyell's case meant not only exploring localities, but also men's minds. No other geologist has qualified more fully in these respects, though, of course, in 1830 he had only made a good beginning. Moreover Lyell, born in 1797, the year in which Hutton died, was a late contemporary of the grand work of William Smith, Cuvier, and Brongniart in stratigraphical palaeontology—of which Hutton had no chance of hearing. Lyell here received no guidance at all from

Hutton; but this was due to an unfortunate accident. Hutton at the time of his death had almost completed a book entitled *Principles of Agriculture*; but the manuscript does not seem to have been looked at by anyone else till 1947. It was then found to contain an amazing discussion, not only of artificial selection, including pure-line selection, but also of natural selection. The gist as regards the latter is conveyed in the following quotation:

To see this beautiful system of animal life (which is also applicable to vegetables) we are to consider, that in the infinite variation of the breed that form best adapted to the exercise of those instinctive arts, by which the species is to live, will be the most certainly continued in the propagation of this animal, and will be always tending more and more to perfect itself by the natural variation which is continually taking place. Thus, for example where dogs are to live by the swiftness of their feet and the sharpness of their sight, the form best adapted to that end will be the most certain of remaining, while those forms that are least adapted to this manner of chase will be the first to perish; and the same will hold good with regard to all the other forms and faculties of the species, by which the instinctive arts of procuring its means of substance may be pursued.

The above is remarkable as the product of a man who died eleven years before Charles Darwin was born, and fully sixty years before the same Darwin weaned Lyell from his belief in the fixity of species; but it must be remembered that Hutton was a contemporary of Charles Darwin's grandfather, Erasmus.

To return to Lyell's treatment of Hutton in his *Principles*. He gives a good picture of the excitement engendered by Hutton's *Theory of the Earth*, which, we are told, was attacked with 'open disregard of candour and temper'; and he points to the widespread fear at the time that any loosening of accepted religious doctrine might lead to excesses such as sadly marred the French Revolution just across the Channel. It is therefore interesting to recall once more that

Hutton, like Friar Generelli, whom Lyell also quotes, was a convinced theist. Within this compass the friar in the mid-eighteenth century declared that we may explain everything 'without violence, without fictions, without hypotheses, without miracles'; while Hutton, somewhat later as we have seen, claimed support for his Uniformitarian doctrine in the assumption that the earth is run on perfect principles, which, being perfect, know no change. He accordingly accepted observation of present-day Nature as affording a safe guide in reconstruction of the past; and to this extent he was now being followed whole-heartedly by Lyell. If we wish to inquire exactly how far Lyell agreed with Hutton's religious concepts, we find that he often gave expression to some of his own, not very different. Darwin, in an autobiography intended only for his children, says Lyell was 'thoroughly liberal in his religious beliefs, or rather disbeliefs; but he was a strong theist. His candour was highly remarkable'. Despite this candour, Lyell was altogether averse to answering back. On the whole he escaped molestation to a wonderful degree, until he found himself among the hornets raised by Darwin's advocacy of evolution in 1858-9.

One feature, especially, of Hutton's Uniformitarian approach rankled with the defenders of religious orthodoxy. It was the *time* he postulated to allow agents of erosion with present-day intensity to develop full-scale scenery. His oft-repeated argument based on perfection would not today be admitted by anyone. His supporting arguments based on observation certainly seemed strong; but even arguments that appear strong must be viewed with suspicion if they lead to an unexpected answer. Moreover the Catastrophists were able to advance what seemed for the time being unanswerable criticisms. Lyell, however, with wide field experience and with full knowledge of what had been said on both sides became a convinced Uniformitarian.

On the way he made some important mistakes; but in spite of them with the publication of his *Principles* he soon led most of the younger generation into the Uniformitarian camp. The conversion of Darwin, twelve years his junior, was particularly rewarding. Darwin, before boarding the *Beagle*, got, on advice from Henslow, in 1831 a copy of the first volume of the *Principles*, to read on his voyage, but on no account to accept. This last caution was disregarded; and the *Principles* undoubtedly greatly helped Darwin to his ultimate conclusion, namely: that the succession of life in earth-history should be ascribed, like all other geological phenomena, to 'natural' causes—a view which we shall soon see was also held by Lyell in 1830, but with a difference.

As pointed out in our own Chapter 2, Hutton's *Theory* was attacked just as much on geological as on theological grounds. Here again the battle was between faith and inquiry—faith in this case inspired by Werner. It is unnecessary to recapitulate the tenets of the Wernerians, or Neptunists, who regarded almost all rocks as deposits from an ocean—with granite the primeval precipitate; or of the Vulcanists, who recognized basalt as volcanic; or yet of the Huttonians or Plutonists, who included even granite among igneous products. Suffice it to say that before Lyell started serious study the contest between water and fire, as it may be termed, had been settled in favour of the latter.

To pass on: in Chapter 5 Lyell holds the Mosaic time scale responsible, as we have just indicated, for belief in catastrophes of intensity quite outside our own experience —a historian brought up to believe that the Great Pyramid was built in a day would naturally ascribe the operation to some superhuman agency.

Lyell also notes with approval Playfair's conclusion that 'change in the animal kingdom seems to be a *part of the order of nature*'—Playfair in this matter was merely agree-

Plate 10   Lyell's sketch of the Temple of Jupiter Serapis at Pozzuoli.

Plate 11 Mrs Lyell.

ing with Cuvier, who held that his many and big Tertiary mammals could not be successfully hiding, alive, today.

On the other hand Lyell rightly criticizes the Plutonists for exaggerating the importance of heat in consolidating sediment, at the expense of pressure and percolating mineral waters—this had been Hutton's greatest blemish.

In Chapters 6 to 9, Lyell expounds a novel theory to account for the life-succession in the rocks of Europe and North America. All admit that during geological time there have been great changes in the distribution of land and sea, and great changes too in local climate. Also all admit that today's local climates are profoundly affected by distribution of land and sea. Accordingly Lyell suggests a correlation between geological changes of local climate and geological redistributions of land and sea. Since, in addition, species-distribution is known to be largely determined by climate, it follows that 'transportations of climate' will contribute to 'local extermination of species'—to be compensated by immigration of other species fitted for the new conditions. Accordingly, the gradual approach to the present distribution of species in our latitudes has been determined by gradual approach to present-day climates, determined in turn by gradual approach to present-day geography. (Geography has other influences besides climatic. Lyell claimed that the Carboniferous lands of the northern hemisphere were oceanic islands, incapable of supporting quadrupeds. The latter, according to his views, were confined to a southern continent.) It will be appreciated that this conception of Lyell's involves the original existence, somewhere or other, of all species of all time— today mostly extinct. For second and third thoughts on this matter one must turn to Volumes 2 and 3.

Lyell's theory agrees with that of the Progressionists led by Cuvier, in assuming fixity of species. It disagrees in that it attributes change of life-assemblages to 'natural'

G

processes of extinction and migration—apart from one notable exception, that of man, whose late creation Lyell excuses as a 'moral', not a 'physical', event. The Progressionists, on the other hand, invoke numerous successions of annihilation and creation—which appears to Lyell shocking. The fossil record, as known at the time, seemed to favour the Progressionists, if one were prepared to admit piecemeal, rather than general, annihilations and creations; but Lyell finds refuge in the manifest imperfections of the record, at the same time citing a number of apparent exceptions to a progressionist sequence. These, we now know, were based upon current misidentifications. At the time, fossil tortoises were supposed to occur in the Old Red Sandstone, dicotyledons in the Carboniferous, and whales in the Lias.

Having explained his view that changes in the organic world have followed upon changes in the inorganic, Lyell devotes the remainder of Volume 1 to *historical* modifications of geography brought about by rivers, springs, and seas (Chapters 10-17), volcanoes (Chapters 18-22) and earthquakes (Chapters 23-26). One might expect a tame story from an arch-enemy of the Catastrophic school; but instead one finds a thriller, crammed with authentic anecdotes of Nature in her wildest moods, leading in one extravagance to the death of sixty thousand people in about six minutes. Examples are quoted from an amazingly wide international field; and many a reader must have been driven to admit that, given time, the activities of the present may well be held responsible for all the achievements of the past. Among geologists Lyell's opposition to von Buch's theory of craters of elevation also attracted much attention. In regard to this we may defer explanation to Chapter 17 (p. 178) where an account is given of two separate visits made by Lyell to Sicily in 1857 and 1858, to check up on evidence furnished by Etna.

1832 Volume 2

Volume 2 carries as frontispiece a picture of the Valle del Bove, Etna. The original was drawn by Lyell on 1 December 1828, while his hat was held on his head by his guide in the wintry wind, and his boots were ominously toasting in hot ashes.

There is again an introductory quotation from Playfair:

The inhabitants of the globe like all the other parts of it, are subject to change. It is not only the individual that perishes, but whole species.

A change in the animal kingdom seems to be part of the order of nature, and is visible in instances to which human power cannot have extended. (Playfair, *Illustrations of the Huttonian Theory*, § 413.)

Then follows a dedication to Broderip, to whom, readers will remember, Buckland owed his introduction to field geology.

Chapters 1-4 are devoted to a statement and criticism of Lamarck's theory of evolution. Lamarck regarded species as arbitrary concepts of convenience. Variation, whether inborn, as 'efforts of internal sentiment', or acquired, as a reaction to environment, was hereditable, with results that know no bound. The changes wrought in domestic-ated plants and animals show what may be expected in Nature.

Lyell contends that species are fixed in the sense that firm limits have been set to the variability of each and every one. Variability is a necessary feature of any species if it is to have a chance of survival in a world itself subject to local change. Variation within a species is hereditable, but only within the limits already fixed by the Creator. Plants and animals, destined for domestication, have been in advance given exceptionally wide limits of variability. They were

planned to accompany man, when eventually this most vari-
able of all species should be commissioned to colonize the
whole world from torrid zone to polar regions.

Chapters 5-7 deal in delightful fashion with the geographical distribution and means of dispersal of species. They
take us back to Lyell's attempt in Volume 1 to explain, by
natural extinction and migration, present and past distribu-
tions of life. The migration was supposed to start from some
unknown complex origin furnished with a full geological
complement of creatures—with the one exception of man
whose creation was to follow. This account in Volume 1
reads as if Lyell imagined at the time that geographical,
including climatic, identity of station would be accompanied by specific identity of population. Clearly such is
not the case, since, for instance, the great majority of
modern species in North America are different from those
found in comparable stations in Europe. Lyell now
(Volume 2) admits that this might suggest to some the
idea of intermittent creations, widely separated in time
and space. On the other hand he argues in parable that
intermittent stray migration confined by 'great natural
barriers' might equally well result in 'distinct botanical
and zoological provinces', and in Chapter 11 he states the
alternatives of intermittent and wholesale creation in impartial manner. We shall be able to explain his position
more clearly when we come to Volume 3.

Chapters 12-18 deal with entombment of fossils and the
influence that life has upon the surface of the earth. He is
quite clear that the geological record proves man to be a
very recent arrival, too late to see a mammoth living—
another conclusion he was destined to revise. His remarks
on surface changes include comments on soil erosion and
on the guidance of atoll growth by submerged crater rims
—a view already favoured by De la Beche, but presently
to be abandoned.

1833 Volume 3

The frontispiece of Volume 3 reproduces another of Lyell's sketches, this time showing the prehistoric vol-canoes of Olot in northeastern Spain (Fig. 9; Pl. 8). It must be realistic, for Lyell in his journal for 1831 records the delight of an Italian refugee on getting a sight of it:

Ah! that is Olot indeed. Well I fought there for thirteen days, five were we encamped on that hill by that church; and so the hollow was the crater, and the cone a volcano. How odd, I never dreamt of that! At its foot we killed 400 of the *factions*! but from that hill, as we passed to enter that valley, a discharge of shot thinned our ranks. We could not return it with any effect, we were on that flat plain, and on the slant of the cone concealed in the vines. There is the defile, through which Milano brought his troops from Gerona, and this is Olot, with its villainous population, of 36,000, all factions.

Volume 3 is dedicated to Murchison, not only for his co-operation in Auvergne, Velay, and Piedmont, but also for his friendly interest in the progress of the *Principles*, interest that had found gratifying expression in two Presi-dential Addresses to the Geological Society, in 1832 and 1833.

The Preface and Chapters 1 and 2 are illuminating, es-pecially in regard to the parts played by divers authors in the elucidation of European Tertiary successions after the first step taken by Cuvier and Brongniart in their descrip-tion of the Paris basin, 1811.

Chapters 3 and 4 consider such essential matters as un-conformities and the possibility of correlating fossil assem-blages belonging to different zoological provinces.

Chapters 5 and 6 launch Lyell's scheme of Tertiary classification (based on the proportion of living species and genera to extinct), which he had developed with Des-hayes; and the latter supplied copious faunal lists. Tertiary time starts for Lyell from the finish of the Chalk period; and ends with the beginning of the Man, or Recent, period. Within its scope there are, as first presented, the Eocene, Miocene, Early Pliocene, and Late Pliocene periods. In after years, Lyell, 1839, renamed Late Pliocene as Pleistocene; while Heinrich Ernst von Beyrich, 1854, transferred parts of the Eocene and Miocene into an independent Oligocene. (Without going into details we may note that both Bronn and Deshayes favoured three divisions of the Tertiary rather than Lyell's original four.)

Chapters 7-20 are devoted to selections of Nature's masterpieces in the form of marine, freshwater, and volcanic phenomena belonging to the various divisions of Recent and Tertiary time. In the main, Lyell is not concerned with the building of a history, so that he starts with the Recent and works backwards, to 'conduct us gradually from the known to the unknown'. However, when he deals with the Eocene of the Paris and London basins, he begins at the beginning. His treatment as a whole awakens in a reader an altogether new realization of the wonders of Tertiary and Recent European geology.

Chapters 21 and 22 discuss the denudation of the Weald. Lyell has now no doubt that vast quantities of chalk have been removed by erosion from the district between the North and South Downs—but mistakenly he thinks the erosion has been mainly marine. He pictures the Wealden area slowly emerging from the sea, and its various strata resisting the surf, each in accordance with its special durability. This last he thinks to have been locally affected by cracks due to earth movement. The chalk escarpments are for him ancient sea-cliffs. The transverse valleys have originated as rents, speedily opened up by marine currents. He knows that the Tertiary as well as the Chalk has been moved; but he holds that, broadly speaking, the long series of elevatory movements was contemporaneous with the deposition of the Tertiaries in the London and Hampshire basins of depression. At this time, and for years afterwards, Lyell considers that Guettard, Desmarest, Hutton, and Playfair had greatly overestimated the efficacy of subaerial erosion. Scrope and a few others protested; but Lyell persisted in his error until Joseph Jukes, 1862, and Andrew Ramsay, 1863, led a renaissance.

Chapter 23 has a little to say about all fossiliferous and associated volcanic rocks of Chalk or earlier date.

Chapter 24 demolishes much of Elie de Beaumont's ideas regarding sudden contemporaneous development of parallel mountain chains.

Chapters 25 and 26 afford good discussions of volcanic, plutonic, and metamorphic problems, drawing largely upon John Macculloch. The word metamorphic is a new introduction based on Hutton's ideas.

At the end of Chapter 26 we read: 'It appears that species have been changed and yet have all been so modelled, on types analogous to those of existing plants and animals, as to indicate throughout a perfect harmony of design and unity of purpose.' Lyell has now definitely become a special type of Recurrent-Creationist, but, strange to say, not a Progressionist. His position in regard to creation is made doubly clear in the following long sentence quoted from a letter to John William Herschel, dated 1836:

When I first came to the notion, which I never saw expressed elsewhere, though I have no doubt it had all been thought out before, of a succession of extinction of species, and creation of new ones, going on perpetually now, and through an indefinite period of the past, and to continue for ages to come, all in accommodation to the changes which must continue in the inanimate and habitable earth, the idea struck me as the grandest which I had ever conceived, so far as regards the attributes of the Presiding Mind.

Lyell's continued opposition to Progressionism is sufficiently illustrated by an 1834 statement taken from Volume 1, third edition, Chapter 9: In the 'succession of quadrupeds, we cannot detect any signs of progressive development of organization'.

Deshayes supplies a 52-page Appendix consisting of Tables of Fossil Shells. The intention of these tables is not to give complete lists of recognized Tertiary species (which at the time numbered 3,036), but to indicate:

426 identified as both Tertiary and Recent.
123 extinct, but known from more than one Tertiary period.
233 limited to one Tertiary period, but known from more than one formation in that period.

This Appendix was repeated in the second edition, 1833, but was omitted from the third and subsequent editions as having been abundantly circulated.

Chapter 9

Professorship – Marriage – Scandinavia – Switzerland

1831 Professorship

We may now resume the personal story, which took us in Chapter 7 to Lyell's return from abroad at the end of 1830, with Volume 1 of the *Principles* safely launched. The reverberations of the new French Revolution were to follow him, leading in Britain to the Reform Act of 1832 and across the Channel to the revolt of Belgium against the rule of Dutch King William. In spite of such distractions Lyell married in 1832, while from 1831-3 he occupied the newly created Chair of Geology at King's College, London.

His father-in-law-to-be, Leonard Horner (1785-1864) was the son of a well-to-do Edinburgh businessman, and had the good fortune to attend Playfair's lectures on mathematics and also to hammer out Huttonian problems on Arthur's Seat. From 1803-14 he lived in London, where, keen on chemistry, mineralogy, and other sciences, he joined the Geological Society in 1808, the second year of its existence. He was soon elected one of its Secretaries, 1810-14; and a Fellow of the Royal Society, 1813. Meanwhile in 1806 he had happily married, and in 1808 had been presented with Mary, the first of six daughters.

In 1814 Horner undertook a business tour to Holland and Saxony on the heels of the evacuating French, demoralized by their recent Russian catastrophe. Thereafter he returned to live for some years in Scotland, where he took an active part in education as well as geology. In 1826 an influential group of public-spirited men set out to found a University of London, claiming that 'the first city in the civilised world is at once the place that most needs a University, and the only great capital which has none'; and they approached Horner, asking him to be Head or Warden. This proposal after due consideration he accepted in May 1827, a fortnight after the laying of the foundation stone.

It is on this occasion that Horner first enters into Lyell's published correspondence. On 10 April we find the latter writing to his father: 'Leonard Horner is in Town from Edinburgh, very *à propos* to keeping me right on my article, as he is a great education man, as well as geologist. His gratitude to me for having got into the "Quarterly Review" an article on the liberal side of geology is very agreeable.'

The institution founded in 1827 continued for some years to be called the University of London; but it was non-sectarian, and its attempt to secure a charter empowering it to confer degrees was bitterly contested. Finally, in 1836, two charters were granted, one incorporating the institution as University College, the other establishing a new body as University of London with authority to grant degrees. Meanwhile in 1829 a rival, Church of England, institution, King's College, was founded, and received its charter without delay. The Chair of Mineralogy and Geology mentioned below was in King's College.

Horner as Warden of the unchartered University approached Lyell to persuade him to be first occupant of this Chair, and on 24 November 1829 received the following refusal:

My friend G. Eyre, a barrister who is attending law lectures at the London University, happened to say this morning that when Lardner spoke of the vacant Chair of Mineralogy and Geology in his introductory lecture, a brother student had mentioned to him that there had been a report of *my* being thought of for it. I ought therefore to tell you that I have always felt it, and do now, to be out of the question; and if the council wish to fill it up, you must consider me quite out of the way, both in justice to the Institution and other candidates. . . . I have not waited till we met, because I did not feel comfortable under the idea that I had let you go away the other day with a notion that I only wanted to be pressed a little. I should like for your sake, and for the science, to see a good man in, but it ought, I believe, to be a man of fortune, who did not hope to pay his travelling expenses by what he made.

All the same by 7 February 1831 we find that Lyell has agreed to accept the Chair, to which he is elected the following month. This information is extracted from a letter to a Scottish geological friend, John Fleming. Lyell explains that he is going to use large diagrams to illustrate his lectures, and hopes that a course of twelve will not prevent him publishing Volume 2 of his *Principles* before his marriage in about a year's time. A letter to Mantell, March 1831, deserves to be quoted in full:

My dear Mantell, — I have been within this last week talked of and invited to be professor of geology at King's College, an appointment in the hands entirely of the Bishop of London, Archbishop of Canterbury, Bishop of Llandaff, and two strictly orthodox doctors, D'Oyley and Lonsdale. Llandaff alone demurred, but as Conybeare sent him (volunteered) a declaration most warm and cordial in favour of me, as safe and orthodox, he must give in or be in a minority of one. The prelates declared 'that they considered some of my doctrines startling enough, but could not find that they were come by otherwise than in a straightforward manner, and (as I appeared to think) logically deducible from the facts, so that whether the facts be true or not, or my conclusions logical or otherwise, there was no reason to infer that I had made my theory from any hostile feeling towards revelation'. Such were nearly their words, yet Featherstonhaugh tells Murchison in a letter, that in the United States he should hardly dare in a review to approve of my doctrines, such a storm would the orthodox raise against him! So much for toleration of Church Establishment and no Church Establishment countries. It is, however, merely a proof of the comparative degree of scientific knowledge diffused. Pray be so kind as to give me the earthquakes. A shock in Sicily which threw down Melazzo, seems to have occurred nearly on, if not on the same day as Dover. Another just announced in China has killed, they say, a million of men, all in favour of modern causes; — it is an ill wind, etc. The young Prince George of Cumberland told me the other day of you and the great lizard, which last has taken much hold of his imagination. 'Tis clear, as Abernethy said, you will ride on that beast. Dont throw away any great big specimens, for if I lecture, I shall be as greedy for them as I have hitherto been shy of them. I will get a scene-painter to put Etna and Auvergne on scenes as large as in a theatre, on canvas from Scrope's and my sketches. Scrope writes, 'If the news be true, and your opinions are to be taken at once into the bosom of the Church, instead of contending against that party for half a century, then, indeed, shall we make a step at once of fifty years in the science—in such a miracle will I believe when I see it performed'.

Ever yours,
Charles Lyell.

It would seem from the above that by this time ecclesiastical headquarters viewed the drying up of Noah's flood as less dangerously subversive than the spread of Lamarck's evolution.

Lyell's first course of lectures was delivered in 1832, and his last in 1833. To begin with he was able to throw his lectures open to the public, including ladies; but before long the college authorities excluded the latter, because their presence 'diverted the attention of the young students'. Attendance dropped disastrously, and Lyell resigned. He felt that his proper place in life was that of gentleman-scientist-author, without strings.

It is, however, only fair to the authorities to point out that Lyell himself had at first planned to exclude the fair sex. 'Grand disputes', he reports, 'at the Geological Society about the propriety of admitting ladies to my lectures. Babbage most anxious to bring his mother and daughter and Lady Guilford; Harris to bring Lady Mary Kerr; and so on. I begged them all not to do so; and they promised, but at last Murchison said, "My wife, however, must come. I promised to bring her, and she would be much disappointed. I will not bring her till the doors are closed." Then they all declared they would too, and so bring the affair to a crisis one way or other.' The privilege seems to have worked wonders among the fair *débutantes*. Mrs Somerville, a famous mathematician, 'was charmed with the effect my first lecture produced on [her daughters] Martha and Mary. They never would read before, but when they came home they set to work in earnest at my two volumes, and examined each other on the points of the lecture.'

Lyell seems to have enjoyed his lectures just about as much as did his audience. 'I have most completely succeeded in my second lecture', he tells a correspondent. Its subject was 'the connection of geology and natural religion'; and later he reports how 'Murchison said today, "I don't know when they will leave off saying that the last is the best lecture of all".'

He was prepared too to answer his critics, and tells how 'Fitton said, "I'm so sorry I missed you last time when the world says you floored Buckland". As Babbage expressed it in a note, "tore Buckland's theory to tatters before his face". But I must say B. showed his good sense, for he has been more goodhumoured since. But he and Sedgwick & Co. blaze away at me so, I can but retaliate.'

Despite the pleasure he received from the plaudits of his friends, Lyell felt that his lectures were of much less permanent importance than his book; and he regretted the time he had to devote to their preparation. Volume 3 was building up slowly—it appeared in April 1833; but his publishers, Murray, put out second editions of Volumes

1 and 2 in January 1832 and 1833 respectively. During his
lifetime the *Principles* as a whole were destined to pass
through eleven editions between 1830 and 1872.

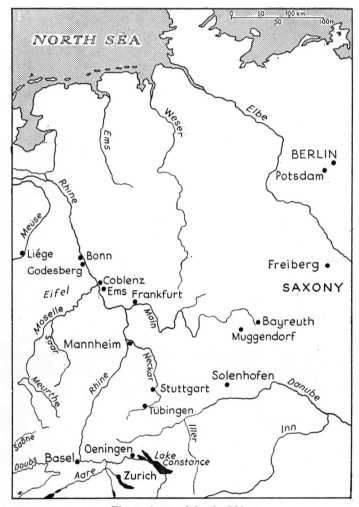

Fig. 10 Approach by the Rhine

Horner severed his connection with London University well in advance of Lyell's resignation. His task was a heavy one, and some of his professors were rebellious. His health suffered, and on doctor's advice in 1830 he spent a fortnight at Ems, near Coblenz, drinking the waters; and then went on to Frankfurt. Here he got news of the Belgian rising, but it did not immediately inconvenience him. Next spring, 1831, he retired; and in June Mrs Horner and four of the daughters set out for Godesberg, near Bonn, leaving Horner with the other two to settle up matters and follow in a couple of months' time. Horner's father had died in 1829, and his only brother several years previously; so that, with his disappointment over London University, he seems to have felt that a temporary change of scene would be welcome.

Mary the first-born was by this time in her twenty-third year, a remarkably pretty girl, and studious too. It seems certain that she and Lyell had come to an understanding before Lyell wrote of his expectation of early marriage in his February letter to Fleming. If so, Mary was probably not surprised at Lyell's choice of the prehistoric volcanoes of Eifel, not very far south from Bonn, as a fit subject for investigation in the early summer of 1831.

Horner, however, had not been consulted. Writing to one of Mary's sisters he confesses to 'more than surprise' at seeing Lyell's hand in Mamma's letter of 10 July. 'He is a most active man, and most zealous geologist, for while other men content themselves with turning over dictionaries, and commentaries, to clear up their difficulties, nothing satisfies him but to cross the sea, and break the rocks of distant mountains to clear up his geological doubts. I shall not be surprised to hear that he is next heard of on the top of the Schnee-Kopf. As to seeing me in Scotland, that is not very likely, for in less than a fortnight, I hope to be back in London. But it must have been a very agreeable surprise to all of you, and you must have enjoyed your distant walks with him very much. I am very sorry that he did not defer his visit until I was with you.'

To Mary herself he writes: 'I leave everything to your decision . . . you have the best possible adviser with you in your dear Mamma.'

And to Lyell, after a visit to Kinnordy and a journey to Godesberg, rendered circuitous by the military situation: 'I am far more proud of having you as a son-in-law than I should have been of any rank or fortune, and I know full well that she will be far more proud of the rank you have obtained as a man of science, than she would have been of any title however noble, or of any fortune however great.'

The above was written on 16 August 1831. By this time France, with the approval of the other great powers, had intervened to secure Belgian independence; but the position was not finally stabilized till 1839. After some months at Godesberg the Horner family moved to an apartment in neighbouring Bonn, where they lived in congenial surroundings for some time to come.

1831-5 Marriage

So in Bonn next year, 12 July 1832, Charles Lyell and Mary Horner were married by a Lutheran clergyman. Afterwards they took a long honeymoon, enjoying scenery, geology, and geologists up the Rhine, across Switzerland, and along Lake Maggiore (Fig. 6). The Rhine loess provided a new experience. Eventually they set up house in London at 16 Hart Street, Bloomsbury, which was to serve as headquarters for the next fourteen happy years.

I have already quoted from Mantell's 1841 correspondence with Silliman of Yale a rather cool appreciation of Lyell's personality. The following excerpts from the same source reveal a distinctly warmer feeling for his consort:

I dined with him last week—a farewell party. His charming little wife (a daughter of Leonard Horner) accompanied him. I have said so much of you and yours to her that she is quite anxious to visit New Haven [U.S.A.]; if she does I am quite sure you will all be delighted with her. . . . About seven or eight years after our acquaintance, Mr. Lyell, with great good sense, abandoned his profession, with his father's consent, and devoted himself wholly to geology, content with a moderate income, and living in a very unostentatious manner in an unfashionable part of the city. A few years ago he married Miss Horner, who is much younger than himself (Lyell is 45 or 46), and a more suitable companion he could not have found. He has no children. . . . I expect Lyell has no servant with him [going to America]; he lives very plainly in London, more so than even I do. My profession compels me to keep a chariot and pair, and I am rather fond of having my house very neat and tasty and my servants well dressed; but Lyell does not care for these things, and is, in truth, quite the philosopher.

There is concealed tragedy in this 1841 appreciation of Mrs Lyell living happily in a philosophical back street. Turning to Mantell's *Journal* we find the first entry for 1835 reading as follows:

April!! — Until this time I have neither had the inclination, nor the leisure to open my note book; alas! the recollection of the past has but few charms for me, and although I have very many blessings bestowed upon me by the Author of all good, yet so chequered is my path, that it were perhaps wise to leave no record of my wanderings. Yet the past months have been the most splendid in my existence, and if fame and reputation could confer happiness, I ought to be happy. Since my residence in Brighton (now about 15 months since) the following pleasing events have occurred:

A piece of Plate presented to me by some of my Lewes Patients.

Two lectures given by me, received with great approbation: elected a Governor of the County Hospital.

An out-doors lecture from Brighton to Newhaven—went off

with great eclat. The Earl of Egremont presented me with £1,000.

A fine specimen of an Iguanodon found at Maidstone, purchased by Mr. Ricardo, H. Smith and other friends, and presented to me free of expense.

The degree of LL.D. conferred on me by the Pres. and Senate of Yale College, Connecticut; and elected an honorary Fellow of the Academy of Sciences.

A work (by Dr. Morton of Philadelphia) on the organic remains of the secondary formations of the United States dedicated to me by the Author.

The Wollaston award (a gold medal worth 10 guineas, and £22 in money) decreed by the Council of the Geological Society.

At the anniversary of the Geol. Society, Mr. Lyell in a very eloquent speech gave an account of my researches.

The contrast revealed in this long quotation becomes understandable when we turn to an 1840 letter to Silliman:

I have no companion—no one whose smile or approbation would cheer me on. . . . There was a time when my poor wife felt deep interest in my pursuits, and was proud of my success, but of late years that feeling had passed away, and she was annoyed rather than gratified by my devotion to science.

Further information is forthcoming from Mantell's annotated *Journal* for 1836-9. Mrs Mantell, who had engraved the illustrations of *The Fossils of the South Downs*, which appeared in 1822, and who the same year had found the first tooth of Iguanodon, had come to feel that her husband's devotion to science had ousted her from his affections. In 1836 their house, No. 20 The Steine, Brighton, was entirely given up to The Sussex Scientific Institution and Mantellian Museum, and in 1839 she finally went her own way.

We have overstepped the time-limit set for the present chapter. Let us return to early August 1831, when Lyell arrived home again in London, an engaged young man.

He set to work immediately, correcting proofs of Volume 2 of his *Principles*. On one occasion we find him being helped in this occupation by his 'steam-engine Hall'; on another he is shaving while the steam-engine reads aloud to him De la Beche's recently published *Manual of Geology*. The steam-engine is the same Hall as two years previously collected butterflies in Auvergne.

Busy as he was, Lyell found time to meet plenty of interesting people. The Reform Bill was a source of great bitterness: 'the fact is there never were such private interests at stake before'. Its passage now seemed inevitable owing to the encouragement given by the 1830 Revolution in France, which produced a reaction in Britain the very reverse of that following the 1789 Revolution with its Reign of Terror. Once passed, the Reform Act would sweep away centuries-old opportunities for lucrative patronage. Its main object was redistribution of representation in parliament, now so hopelessly out of date that Cornwall returned forty-two members against Scotland's forty-five; Old Sarum two against Manchester's none.

On 1 September Lyell took the steamer for Leith; and once in Edinburgh called on friends old and new, including the leading local research geologist, Charles Maclaren, 'that furious radical as Editor of the "Scotsman", and a mild, amicable, simple-minded man in private'.

A few days later he was at sister-full Kinnordy, followed by Hall. Proofs, butterflies, bees, plants, politics, and social gaieties filled his days. In spite of his liberal proclivities he had been appointed Deputy-Lieutenant of the County of Angus.

His youngest sisters were thrilled at the prospect of a county ball at Forfar, planned for 10 October; but this was suddenly abandoned, with only two days' notice. It had transpired that the townsfolk were resolved to smash to pieces all the Tory carriages assembled for the fête if, as anticipated, news came through that the Lords had thrown out the Reform Bill. Actually, such rioting as occurred before the delayed passing of the Act next year was nowhere serious. The death of George IV in 1830 and the accession of the comparatively harmless sailor-king, William IV, had greatly eased the situation. While others worried, Lyell found himself in the fortunate position of Voltaire's gardener: working, without thinking, the only way to be happy.

Back to town at the start of November, Lyell had to answer many friends who inquired what precise page of his Volume 2 has been printed. Before long he decided to develop this proposed final volume into Volumes 2 and 3; which enabled him to lay Volume 2 on the table of the Geological Society on 6 January 1832; with Volume 3 to follow.

Broderip, when told of Lyell's intention to dedicate Volume 2 to him, was overjoyed, asserting that a legacy of £5,000 would have given less pleasure. After the event Lyell tells us: 'Babbage [inventor of calculating machines] and Fitton were so delighted at seeing my volume dedicated to a private friend, instead of some great man, that in the effusion of their feeling of friendship for Broderip, and their anti-aristocrat feeling of independence they came up, and each shook me by the hand, saying, "I am as much obliged to you as if you had done me a favour".'

At the time, feeling was running high against Court interference in the affairs of the Royal Society. Towards the end of 1830, Davies Gilbert retired from the Presidency of the Society to make way for the Duke of Sussex, sixth son of George III. Murchison was active in persuading Herschel to allow his name to go forward in opposition; and Lyell co-operated. Sedgwick, whom Sussex had chosen as personal chaplain, took no 'public steps', but wrote a 'very strong' letter to the Duke expressing his private views. Still the Duke persisted, and was elected by 119 votes to 111. He sent a kindly reply to Sedgwick, and in his first Presidential Address referred to the honour, he could not call it a misfortune, of having been opposed by so distinguished a man as Sir John Herschel. He presided regularly at meetings; and in after years Lyell congratulated Science in having so narrowly escaped the danger of losing Herschel's survey of the stars of the southern hemisphere.

To return to the close of 1831. Lyell found the Murchisons in high fettle. The first attack upon the Welsh marches was promising well; and the first meeting of the British Association at York had proved a great success. Murchison was President of Section C (Geology and Geography), and demonstrated to it the results he had just obtained in the field. Following valuable work by local geologists, he had advanced into transitional terrain on Smithian lines, and was establishing a new system, Silurian, emerging with numerous fossiliferous horizons from beneath conformable Old Red Sandstone. Accordingly his new system had, from the beginning, a defined top, though not a defined base. In full agreement Murchison's great friend, Sedgwick, had concurrently resumed his attack upon Transition rocks, this time in North Wales instead of the Lake District. He started well away from the Old Red Sandstone, in rocks that were older than Murchison's. He too was bent upon erecting a new system on Smithian lines. Sedgwick's Cambrian started with the twofold disadvantage of having neither top nor bottom settled. In years to come this was to lead to lamentable strife, for the two great empire builders failed to agree on a frontier separating their systems.

Lyell found it 'cheering' to note Murchison's 'unabated ardour'. On the other hand, after listening to Sedgwick declaring it 'very dry work geologizing in Wales, all primary and old rocks, like rubbing yourself on a grinding stone', he felt that this master of stratigraphy was 'wasting his giant strength'. Actually, Sedgwick's grumbles should not have been taken seriously; they were habitual, generally concerning the state of his ill health. The results he secured in Wales richly rewarded the labours of the chase. Incidentally, we may recall that young Darwin accompanied Sedgwick for two or three weeks in this Welsh adventure, and thus acquired the rudiments of geological exploration in the field before boarding the *Beagle* at the end of the year.

One event above all others makes 1831 shine in the annals of British Geology. In it Sedgwick, as retiring President of the Geological Society, seized the opportunity to acknowledge William Smith as Father of English Geology. The occasion was the presentation of the first Wollaston Medal; and it was indeed a happy coincidence that the ceremony devolved on one who so sincerely appreciated his own filial indebtedness and that of others; and who was not afraid to voice his admiration in appropriate terms. His tribute is often quoted and rewards all who read it.

In his Presidential Address which followed, Sedgwick extended a warm, but critical, welcome to Lyell's recently published Volume 1:

> Were I to tell him of the instruction I received from every chapter of his work, and of the delight with which I rose from the perusal of the whole, I might seem to flatter rather than to speak the language of sober criticism; but . . . I could not but regret [that he seems to stand as] the champion of the leading doctrine of the Huttonian hypothesis. . . . According to the principles of Mr. Lyell, the physical operations now going on, are not only the type, but the measure of intensity, of the physical powers acting on the earth at all anterior periods.

One more event of 1831 may be recalled in passing: the submarine eruption that built up Graham Island off the coast of Sicily. The Geological Society greatly enjoyed a first-hand account by the Prussian Hoffman forwarded in English by Horner: 'The structure of Pantellaria', says Lyell, 'the washing away of the new isle, the par-boiled fish, the floating cinders, the clefts at Sciacca, etc., all afforded subjects for Fitton, myself, De la Bêche, Dr. Babington, Murchison, and others to dilate upon.'

Presently 1831 closes, and on its last day we find Lyell writing to his betrothed:

If I could secure a handsome profit in my work, I should feel more free from all responsibility in cutting my cables at King's College. Do not think that my views in regard to science are taking a money-making, mercantile turn. What I want is to secure the power of commanding *time* to advance my knowledge and fame, and at the same time to feel that in so doing I am not abandoning the interests of my family, and earning something more substantial than fame. I am never so happy as when at the end of a week I feel that I have employed every day in a manner that will tell to the rest of my life, and last week will, I think, be one of them.

We have already noted the main events of 1832: the publication of Volume 2; the lectures at King's College; the wedding; the honeymoon; the new home in London. A few additional touches will lend colour to the picture. Brother Tom had been on leave and was then just starting off for the West Indies. He had roughed it indeed, with shipwreck, fever, and a tyrannical captain, 'so violent that he has broken more than one five-guinea telescope on the *heads* of the sailors, and sworn at his first lieutenant before the crew'.

Steam-engine Hall gave less cause for concern, but one day both Lyell and he felt need of a rest. They boarded a coach, Lyell inside and Hall out, and visited the farm of the Zoological Society at Kingston Hill to see kangaroos, quaggas, emus, etc.; and so on to the adjoining 'Coombe

Wood, classical ground to entomologists. . . . We found some black beetles, and I found that Hall remembered the exact names—it is wonderful how fond he is of entomology. I should never make him take to geology in the same way. He has planned himself a nice wire net-hoop, which goes into his hat, and takes out and fits into a walking-stick'.

In June 1833, Lyell, with influenza, Volume 3, and lecture courses at both the Royal Institution and ladyless King's safely past, started off with his wife on a three-month excursion to the Continent. In Paris Mary was introduced at Montmartre to the subterranean galleries in gypsum, which had provided Cuvier with many of his skeletons, and the municipality with favourable sites for sewers. They next made for the Rhine at Bonn, and moved upstream to Mannheim (Fig. 10); then south and east by Stuttgart to visit quarries at Solenhofen in Jurassic lithographic stone—famous fossils in rare preservation had already been found, but not as yet *Archaeopteryx*, linking reptiles and birds. From Solenhofen they made northeast to Bayreuth for the bear-bone caves of Muggendorf advertised by Buckland; and so, by Frankfurt, Liége, and Calais, home.

His call at Liége was probably the most fruitful incident, and is well described in a letter to Mantell:

I have just arrived from Dover, having passed through Belgium in my way. I saw there at Liége the collection of Dr. Schmerling, who in *three years* has, by his own exertions and the incessant labour of a clever amateur servant, cleared out some twenty caves untouched by any previous searcher, and has filled a truly splendid museum. He numbers already thrice the number of fossil cavern mammalia known when Buckland wrote his 'Idola specus'; and such is the prodigious number of the individuals of some species, the bears for example, of which he has five species, one large, one new, that several entire skeletons will be constructed. Oh, that the Lewes chalk had been cavernous! And he

has these and a number of yet unexplored, and shortly to be
investigated holes, all to himself. But envy him not—you can
imagine what he feels at being far from a metropolis which can
afford him sympathy: and having not one congenial soul at Liége,
and none who take any interest in his discoveries save the priests
—and what kind *they* take you may guess more especially as he
has found human remains in breccia, embedded with the extinct
species, under circumstances far more difficult to get over than
any I have previously heard of. The *three* coats or layers of
stalagmite cited by me at Choquier are true. Talking of the
priests, they have obtained grants for new monkish establish-
ments in Liége, while the University of Ghent falls to the ground,
and the Protestant professors are cashiered, and King William's
patronage of natural history excluded. The movement [revolt of
Belgium against William of Orange] was mainly one of Catholic
bigots against a king who wished to introduce schools, and who,
whatever faults he committed, was of all European sovereigns
the greatest promoter and most judicious patron of physical
science. Leopold has nothing left for it but to lean on the priests,
reinforced as they are by the Jesuits exiled from France. But as
yet the Belgian press is free; with that there is always hope.

Lyell had already shown an interest in the bone-caves of
Sicily—who could resist them? Now, following his specially directed visits to Muggendorf and Liége, it is fair to
say that 1833 saw not only the completion of his first great
book, the *Principles*, but also the start, perhaps subcons-
cious, of his second, *The Antiquity of Man*.

1834-5 Scandinavia and Switzerland

The Royal Society set its seal of approval on the
Principles by awarding Lyell a Royal Medal in 1834.

Meanwhile in May the same year, this earnest seeker
after truth started for a ten-week solo in Scandinavia. He
was determined to judge for himself the validity of claims
concerning tranquil upheaval of most of Sweden, continuing till today. Celsius, early in the eighteenth century,

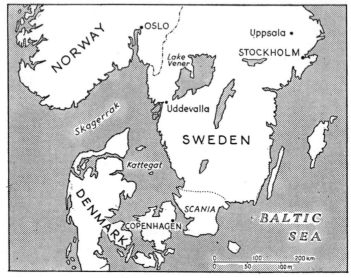

Fig. 11 Southern Scandinavia

had published *Observations on the diminution of the Waters of the Baltic and German Ocean*; and these Playfair, a hundred years later in his *Illustrations*, had reinterpreted as evidence of circumscribed elevation of land rather than of general withdrawal of water. (Even in the first edition of his *Principles*, 1830, Lyell gives five pages to the 'Celsian controversy with its many contestants', and refers readers to von Hoff for a fuller account. In Volume 2 of the fourth edition, 1835, he makes it the subject of chapter 17 nineteen pages long.)

Arrived in Denmark, Lyell found much to interest him in comparing the local Upper Cretaceous with developments he had seen the past year in Belgium, bridging to some extent the gap between English Chalk and Tertiaries. He was, however, even more impressed with the number and size of erratics in the Diluvium. Crown Prince

Christian too was well worth meeting: his Treasurer, we are told, found it 'no easy matter to manage his finances as the Prince could not resist when a good shell or mineral was offered'.

Lyell asked Prince Christian 'how Sweden, having only a few inhabitants, and so little a literary country, had done so much for science. He said, "Because the universities were endowed with much of the wealth of the church, and there is an independence for men who, if they love science, may devote themselves for life to it".' This was of course only a partial answer, since similar endowment of Oxford and Cambridge had on the whole favoured other outlets.

On crossing to Sweden, Lyell was very fortunate in purchasing a serviceable light carriage and in securing an excellent interpreter, who came largely for the fun of the journey, and whose only fault was a tendency to oversleep of a morning. Roads (without turnpikes) and stage horses were both of them good. It was a duty incumbent on the peasantry to make wheeled intercourse possible.

Lyell's investigation of upheaval, in which he received sympathetic assistance from the great chemist Berzelius and several others, had three main aspects: namely to check:

(1) geologically recent, relative elevation;
(2) its actual continuance till today; and
(3) its localization, pointing to uneven earth-movement.

(1) It was easy to verify the existence of beds with modern shells high above present sea-level. Lyell recognized also that the high-level shells near Stockholm and Uppsala are of Baltic types, while those near the junction of Skagerrak and Kattegat are such as live today in more saline waters. Among these latter he repeated Brongniart's valuable observation of barnacles still attached to rock surfaces.

(2) It was much more difficult to be sure of relating change of average sea-level accomplished during the past few years, for the waters of both Baltic and Kattegat, though tideless, stand at appreciably different heights according to wind, barometric pressure, rain, and thaw. Lyell visited a number of bench-marks engraved on rock surfaces (mainly in 1820), and questioned all who seemed trustworthy witnesses. He was thoroughly critical; but was soon completely satisfied concerning 'the great northern phenomenon' of relative upheaval unaccompanied by earthquakes, at a rate to be measured sometimes in feet per century.

(3) Lack of evidence of corresponding relative upheaval in Scania, the southern tip of Sweden, showed that the phenomena observed farther north could not be attributed to a general withdrawal of the sea.

Lyell once more was greatly impressed by erratics, and saw that their transport was of geologically recent date. Some of their carry on the modern shore was certainly due to present-day floating by ice, and he naturally extended this explanation to boulders that today lie well above high water mark. He had already in Volume 3, Chapter II, of the *Principles* (first edition, 1833) invoked icebergs floating on floods discharged from imaginary lakes, temporarily dammed by imaginary landslips, to carry Mont Blanc erratics to the summit of Salève overlooking Geneva (cf. Fig. 14)—so he was prepared for anything! Still, from now on, his tendency was to dispense with catastrophic torrents, and to allow ice-floes quietly to move and remove boulders during various stages of submergence. This was quite in keeping with an insertion he had already made in Volume 1 of the third edition of the *Principles*, 1834, in which he points out that icebergs laden with moraine are constantly floated off where glaciers of high latitudes enter the sea.

After rejoining his wife at Kinnordy Lyell presented his ideas regarding both elevation and floating ice to the British Association meeting in Edinburgh; and later in the year to the Royal Society in London which received it in the form of a Bakerian Lecture.

At the start of next year, 1835, Lyell agreed to his publisher's request for a small simple book to be called *The Elements of Geology*. Then in February he accepted appointment as President of the Geological Society. This post he held for two sessions involving the delivery of long Addresses at Anniversary Meetings in February 1836 and 1837.

To return to 1835: in June a fourth edition of the *Principles* was published, now in four volumes. It represents a very considerable recast of the original, entailing much work on the part of the author. Though 2,000 copies were printed, it was destined to be sold out in about a year's time.

In July Lyell started off with Mrs Lyell, a very real help, on a three-month excursion to be spent mainly in Switzerland. Jules Thurmann, the great local expert in the north, gave 'in a short time a beautiful insight into the structure, on which he has published'; and Lyell 'was glad to verify his observations in the field, and to see his beautiful collection of Jurassic fossils'.

Lyell had originally intended to go on to Glarus (north of the upper Rhine); but, finding the Alps really difficult, he was held up instead for six weeks in the Bernese Oberland (the district of Grindelwald, etc., Fig. 6), which he studied with the help of a map and memoir by Bernhard Studer. The trip ended in September with attendance at the German Scientific Association meeting in Bonn. The Chair of the geological section was occupied on successive days by von Buch, Buckland, de Beaumont, and Lyell.

Chapter 10

Lyell-Darwin Combine

We must now reintroduce Charles Darwin into our story. We have already told in Chapter 8 how he obtained on Henslow's advice a copy of Volume 1 of the *Principles* to read during the voyage of the *Beagle*, which started on 27 December 1831—the second volume reached Darwin at Montevideo, in November 1832.

Volume 1 brought to Darwin an altogether new understanding of what geology really meant. This can best be judged from his own words: 'The very first place which I examined, St. Iago, in the Cape de Verde islands, showed me clearly the wonderful superiority of Lyell's manner of treating geology compared with that of any other author whose work I had with me or ever afterwards read.' Darwin spent three weeks at St Iago, and a letter to Henslow supplies a contemporary statement: 'The geology was pre-eminently interesting; there are some facts on a large-scale of upraised coast (which is an excellent epoch for all the volcanic rocks to date from), that would interest Mr. Lyell.'

This beginning is typical of the whole voyage, continued for five years. It does not mean that Darwin surrendered his judgment: his extension of previous knowledge of modern earth-movements in South America was indeed thoroughly Lyellian; but his reference of atolls to recent earth-movements (subsidence) in the Pacific and

116

Indian Oceans caused Lyell a 'pang', accompanying acceptance.

Perhaps the most important of Darwin's geological observations made during the voyage was his recognition that recently extinct South American mammals are, as a rule, thoroughly South American in character—a recognition which continued Cuvier's demonstration of analogies connecting *Megatherium* with the sloths of today. We shall presently quote Lyell's appreciation of Darwin's discovery on this matter. Meanwhile let us acknowledge that Lyell himself deserves a share of the credit; for it was he who had turned Darwin into an enthusiastic geologist, one who soon came to prefer a hammer to a gun. Judd has emphasized that Darwin did not have to wait in this particular case for expert examination of his fossils. In a letter to Henslow dated 24 December 1832, Darwin says: 'I have been very lucky with fossil bones; I have fragments of at least six distinct animals. . . . Immediately I saw them I thought they must belong to an enormous armadillo, living species of which genus are very common here.'

A great deal of Darwin's work concerned volcanoes. In this again his treatment of the subject derived inspiration from Lyell. Darwin's gratitude found expression again and again in after years. When, for instance, in 1845 he published the second edition of his *Journal of Researches*, now appearing as a separate book, he dedicated it to Lyell, with the explanation: 'The chief part of whatever scientific merit this journal and the other works of the author may possess, has been derived from studying the well-known and admirable *Principles of Geology*.'

During his voyage Darwin sent home batches of notes and specimens to Henslow's safe keeping. Some of the notes were communicated by Sedgwick at a Geological Society meeting on 18 November 1835. No wonder we find Lyell in a letter to Sedgwick in December exclaiming:

'How I long for a return of Darwin! I hope you do not
mean to monopolize him at Cambridge.'

Lyell's 1836 Address. At the Geological Society's Anniversary Meeting, in February 1836, Lyell had the congenial task of announcing the award of the Wollaston Medal
to Louis Jean Rudolphe Agassiz (1807-73), the already
great, though young, Swiss authority on fish, fresh and
fossil; and of the Wollaston fund to his own valued colla-
borator in Tertiary stratigraphy, Gérard Paul Deshayes.

Lyell then turned to his Presidential Address and,
following custom, reviewed the geological achievements
of the past year, expanding along lines of special interest.
The following quotation records the foundation in 1835
of the Geological Survey of England, which, like the
Geological Society itself, was the first of its kind in the
world:

Early in the spring of last year application was made by the
Master General and Board of Ordnance to Dr. Buckland and
Mr. Sedgwick, as Professors of Geology in the Universities of
Oxford and Cambridge, and to myself, as President of this
Society, to offer our opinion as to the expediency of combining
a geological examination of the English counties with the geographical survey now in progress. In compliance with this re-
quisition we drew up a joint report, in which we endeavoured to
state fully our opinion as to the great advantages which must
accrue from such an undertaking not only as calculated to pro-
mote geological science, which would alone be a sufficient object,
but also as a work of great practical utility, bearing on agriculture, mining, road-making, the formation of canals and rail-
roads, and other branches of national industry. The enlightened
views of the Board of Ordnance were warmly seconded by the
present Chancellor of the Exchequer, and a grant was obtained
from the Treasury to defray the additional expenses which will
be incurred in colouring geologically the Ordnance county maps.
. . . This end, however, could only be fully accomplished by

securing the co-operation of an experienced and able geologist, who might organize and direct the operations, and I congratulate the Society that our Foreign Secretary, Mr. de la Beche, has been chosen to discharge an office for which he is so eminently qualified.

Lyell, continuing, drew attention to Sedgwick's recognition that 'three distinct forms of structure are exhibited in certain rocks throughout large districts': namely, stratification, joints, and slaty cleavage. He was also able to announce the forthcoming publication of Murchison's *Silurian System*, based on five years of survey. (This, however, was delayed till towards the close of 1838.)

After these and other points had been made, Lyell passed to his two pet subjects of the day: earth-movement and dispersal of erratics:

> Few communications have excited more interest in the Society than the letters on South America addressed by Mr. Charles Darwin to Professor Henslow. . . . Scattered over the whole [area examined], and at various heights above the sea, from 1300 feet downwards, are recent shells of *littoral* species of the neighbouring coast, so that every part of the surface seems once to have been a shore, and Mr. Darwin supposes that an upheaval to the amount of 1300 feet has been owing to a succession of small elevations, like those experienced in modern times in Chili.

Strangely contradictory reports had been received as to whether or no recent Chilean earthquakes had really been accompanied by uplift. In regard to the latest big quake of 20 February 1835, there could be no doubt, for upheaval had been attested on oath by Captain Robert Fitzroy of the *Beagle* in the course of a court-martial resulting from the wreck of the frigate *Challenger* on an uncharted reef.

Concerning erratics, floating ice was once more advocated as the agent of dispersal. Here a very interesting feature of Lyell's address was 'recognition that Venetz and Charpentier have attributed transport of erratics in

I

Switzerland to glaciers more extensive than they are to-day'. For detail he referred readers to a paper by Charpentier. (He added, 'Mr. Bakewell· has also in some of his works alluded to the carrying of Alpine blocks by ice'— but so too had Lyell when talking of moraines.) We shall return to Ignace Venetz and Jean G. F. de Charpentier in Chapter 12.

It must be confessed that much of Lyell's argument from now onwards concerning recent submergence in Britain is vitiated by his unawareness of vanished glaciers capable of lifting and carrying sea-shells along with other erratics. He tells us of a distinction Murchison draws between a local Welsh drift without northern erratics or shells and a Lancashire-Cheshire drift with both these conspicuous contents; but he has no better explanation to offer than that submergence seems to have been localized.

Darwin's Return. In May 1836 Lyell was called upon by his publishers to interrupt other scientific activities and prepare a fifth edition of his *Principles.* This with his *Elements* and his second Presidential Address still ahead must have kept him busy. He spent two months at Kinnordy followed by one in Arran, where by chance he had the company of young Andrew Ramsay, future Director General of the Geological Survey.

Soon after Lyell got back to London, Darwin arrived home on 2 October 1836; and on 30 November was elected a fellow of the Geological Society. This was eighteen years before he joined the Linnean; but we must remember that in 1837 he opened his first notebook on Transmutation of Species.

Darwin lost little time in submitting a paper for Lyell's consideration dealing with recent elevation on the coast of Chile. Thus we find Lyell writing back on 26 December asking Darwin to dinner on 2 January 1837, when they could talk over certain suggested alterations. This letter is well known for its advice to Darwin 'to work as I did, exclusively for yourself and for your science for many years, and do not prematurely incur the honour, or penalty, of official dignities'.

Lyell's wish expressed to Sedgwick was granted early fulfilment. In the spring of 1837 Darwin migrated to London to remain there, very happily, till his removal to Down in 1842. On the other hand Darwin found himself pressed into service as a Secretary to the Geological Society, 1838-41, endowing that post with undying honour.

Lyell's 1837 Address. The paper which Darwin had submitted to Lyell was presented at the Society on 14 January 1837. It was followed in February by Lyell's second Presidential Address, from which we need only select three points for notice.

(1) In again parading evidence for recent earth-movement Lyell cites Darwin as principal witness.

(2) After detailing wonderful discoveries of fish, reptiles, and mammals, which Proby Thomes Cautley and Hugh Falconer (who received the year's Wollaston Medal in duplicate) had made on the banks of the tributaries of the Indus and Ganges, Lyell narrates how

Darwin was employed in collecting the bones of large extinct mammalia, near the banks of the Rio Plata, in the Pampas of Buenos Ayres and in Patagonia. Mr. Owen has enabled me to announce to you . . . a cranium with teeth of the Megatherium . . . another animal as large as an ox, and allied to the Megatherium . . . a third creature of the order Edentata . . . in the shape of a gigantic Armadillo, as large as a Tapir . . . a gigantic Llama from the plains of Patagonia, which must have been as large as a camel and with a longer neck; and lastly, of the rodentia there is the cranium of a huge animal of the size of a rhinoceros, with some modification in the form of the skull resembling that of a Wombat.

These fossils, of which a description will shortly be given by Messrs. Clift and Owen, establish the fact that the peculiar type of organization which is now characteristic of the South American mammalia has been developed on that continent for a long period.

(3) The third point does not concern Darwin at all. In his previous address Lyell had bestowed well merited praise on De la Beche, but this does not prevent him now from administering equally well merited criticism for departure from William Smith's teaching. De la Beche in 1834 had found that the Culm Measures of Devon contain Carboniferous plants; and yet, because of the troubled condition of their strata, had interpreted them as a pre-Silurian formation. Against this Sedgwick and Murchison had protested, claiming at the Bristol meeting of the British Association, 1836, that the fossil evidence was conclusively supported by structural evidence. Their intervention, Murchison tells us, raised grumbles from Greenough, Buckland, and the old set. Continuing, De la Beche next sought to justify his position by pointing to a supposed discovery by de Beaumont in the Alps of Carboniferous plants on the same horizon as Liassic shells. This Lyell counters in his Address recalling his experiences of 1835:

You are not ignorant that the strata of the Alps are involved in extreme confusion, and complexity, mountain masses having been completely overturned and twisted, so that the same set of strata have been found at the top and bottom of the same section separated by several thousand feet of beds belonging to an older formation.

Lyell writing to Sedgwick the following April (1837) hopes that he approves of this handling of the Devon affair; and wishes that his old friend 'were more and oftener in town. It is rare even in one's own pursuits to meet with congenial souls, and Darwin is a glorious addition to my [? any] society of geologists'.

Lyell continued in London till early summer, and lit on the happy idea of unloading some of the cargo of his

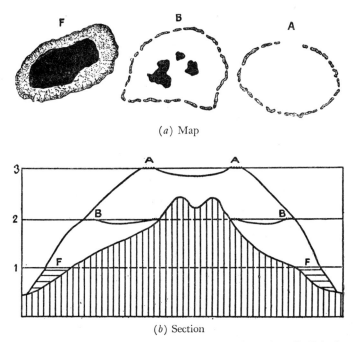

(a) Map

(b) Section

Fig. 12 Darwin's submergence theory of atoll formation. F. Fringing reef; B. Barrier reef; A. Atoll; the numbers 1, 2, and 3 show the successive sea-levels. A sinking island-nucleus is shown black on the map and vertically ruled in section.

Principles, mostly the stratigraphical matter of Volume 4 of the fifth edition (which had appeared in March) into the projected *Elements.* He also found great pleasure in Darwin's theory of atolls (see Fig. 12) and in some experiments on primitive telegraphy which Wheatstone was conducting in the crypt of King's College.

Chapter 11

Scandinavia
Elements – Palaeozoic Confusion – Glen Roy

1837-8 Scandinavia – *Elements* – Palaeozoic Confusion

When June 1837 came Lyell and his wife started on a long excursion to Denmark and Norway (Fig. 11), and home by Paris, reaching London on 28 September. His main employment was the revision of shell determinations with the help of Henrick Henricksen Beck, Prince Christian's naturalist; and he was able in many cases to consult Linnaeus' types. In Norway he was much impressed by the clear manner in which granite near Oslo intruded fossiliferous Transitionals.

The return from Paris was made by train to St Germain, by steamer down the Seine to Havre, and so on across the channel. The railway was at this time a joyous novelty for Parisians. 'Fortunately, every one of the engineers as well as the engines are English, and not one accident has happened, though as many as 10,000 a day have travelled for four weeks since it has opened. . . . Our train contained 1,200 persons, each carriage forty, and many being filled with well-dressed ladies and beaux, was a very gay sight.'

The accession of Queen Victoria meant little to Lyell. The only references to it in his published letters concern dinner table talk about the impossibility of separating Hanoverian and English jewels now that the crowns have come apart, and the good style the Queen had shown during the coronation pageant.

The appearance of the *Elements of Geology* provided a landmark for the spring of 1838. Part I in Chapters 1-11 distributes rocks according to character into four great classes: aqueous; volcanic; plutonic; metamorphic. Part II in Chapters 12-25 redistributes them into age-groups: Recent, Tertiary, Cretaceous, etc. There is very much less physical and biological geography than in the *Principles*.

There are 294 figures in the text as against 226 all told in the four volumes of the fifth edition of the *Principles*; and many of them are pictures of fossils. Thus we find Lyell writing to Sedgwick: 'I am now upon your Cambrians and as I give a few woodcuts of fossils in each group I should have liked to have given a few of the earliest ones if possible.' The answer to this request is almost certainly Figure 283 of the *Elements*. It portrays an Upper Devonian Clymeniid cephalopod newly described from Sedgwick's own collection of Cornish fossils from below the Culm Measures! At the time, the rocks in this position were wrongly regarded by Sedgwick and Murchison as of Cambrian age, owing to misidentification of fossils for which they were not responsible. The muddle, as it happened, was already in process of correction. William Lonsdale, the gifted Curator of the Geological Society's Museum, had realized in December 1837 that certain sub-Culm fossils are of types intermediate between those characteristic of the Carboniferous and the Silurian systems; so that the containing rocks might well be contemporaneous with the Old Red Sandstone, in spite of lithological and faunal contrasts. This brilliant suggestion, which he talked over with Murchison, Sedgwick, De la Beche, and others, was adopted by the two former in a paper read at the Society in April 1839. One result was the introduction of the name Devonian to cover the Old Red Sandstone and contemporary marine formations.

It is very doubtful whether in 1838 Sedgwick could have provided Lyell with any fossil except *Lingulella davisii* from what he called his Lower Cambrian. In the abstract of a paper presented to the Society in March and May 1838, he mentions no Cambrian fossil by name, but says that many belonging to the Upper division 'are identical in species with those of the Lower division of the *Silurian System,* nor have the true distinctive zoological characters of the group been well ascertained'. It is clear that he had not yet suspected that his Upper Cambrian and Murchison's Lower Silurian were, broadly speaking, synonymous. In fact for several years to come comparison between the two was vitiated by an internal miscorrelation, for which Murchison was responsible. Thus not till the early '50s did the question arise as to whether Sedgwick's classification should or should not replace Murchison's, in major features as well as in detail. Sedgwick's was based on correct determination of local succession in the field, but only laggardly accompanied by published lists of fossils; Murchison's, though admittedly muddled, had been from the first combined with fossil lists, which made it international, though, of course, subject to correction. The sad result was a fierce controversy that continued till after both protagonists had passed away.

One of the most exasperating features of the intervening years dates from 1845. Sedgwick, writing *On the Older Palaeozoic* (*Protozoic*) *Rocks of North Wales,* and wishing to show that the boundary between Cambrian and Silurian was not as yet decided, mapped all formations older than the Upper Silurian as *Protozoic = Lower Silurian + Cambrian.* This, before printing, was changed *without consultation* by Henry Warburton to *Protozoic =*

Lower Silurian! Sedgwick did not notice what had happened till long afterwards, when naturally he was furious. The happy ending, as most think, came eventually in 1879, when Charles Lapworth introduced Ordovician to cover the division in dispute. Not so happy, retorted Thomas McKenny Hughes, Sedgwick's biographer, 'One shell is given to Sedgwick, the other to Murchison, but who gets the oyster?'

1838-9 Newcastle B.A. and Glen Roy

In August 1838 the Lyells turned northwards for the British Association Meeting at Newcastle. On the way they stopped to re-investigate ever-present problems of the Crag in Suffolk and Norfolk. This so-called Crag is an unconsolidated shelly deposit. Lyell always grouped it as Pliocene, but today most of it has been transferred to early Pleistocene. Arrived at Newcastle Lyell found himself elected President of the Geological Section. Enthusiasm was rampant. The daily attendance at the Section was from 1,000 to 1,500; while 3,000 described by Herschel as 'colliers and rabble (mixed with a sprinkling of their employers)' flocked to the seashore to listen to the eloquence of Sedgwick.

Once at Kinnordy, Lyell, wearying for his Darwin, supplied him with details of how to make the journey to achieve reunion. He tells too of his father's delight over Darwin's *Journal*, which was to be bound and given as a present to the older Hooker, Sir William.

Do not let Broderip, or the 'Times', or the 'Age', or 'John Bull', nor any papers, whether of saints or sinners, induce you to join in running down the British Association. I do not mean to insinuate that you ever did so, but I have myself often seen its faults in a strong light, and am aware of what may be urged against philosophers turning public orators, etc. But I am convinced, although it is not the way I love to spend my own time, that in this country no importance is attached to any body of men who do not make occasional demonstrations of their strength in public meetings. It is a country where, as Tom Moore justly complained, a most exaggerated importance is attached to the faculty of thinking on your legs, and where, as Dan O'Connell well knows, nothing is to be got in the way of homage or influence, or even a fair share of power, without agitation. . . . Go next year to Birmingham if you can, although your advisor has been only to two out of eight meetings.

In the same letter Lyell discusses the 'Parallel Roads' of Glen Roy (Pl. 12), which both he and Darwin regarded as spectacular examples of raised sea-beaches recalling what can be seen along the slopes of the Andes. Darwin in June had spent eight good days in the Glen Roy district.

The fame of the Parallel Roads has been so loudly sung that one is apt to approach them with a certain anxiety; but all misgiving vanishes when, after travelling a short way up the glen, one sees the three terraces traced along the hillsides with a simplicity that defies pictorial exaggeration. The only feeling that remains is: 'Behold, the half was not told us!' The best impression of what the Parallel Roads look like in nature is furnished by Macculloch's plates in the *Transactions of the Geological Society*, 1817. Sir Archibald Geikie's sketch in his *Scenery of Scotland*, 1901 is also useful (see Fig. 13). Their extent and their relation to the valley system of the district are indicated in Figure 15.

The Parallel Roads are old beach-lines. There are three in Glen Roy at levels of 1,155, 1,077 and 862 feet respectively above sea-level. A similar terrace at 1,178 feet is also met with in the adjacent valley of Glen Gloy. Each strand-line corresponds in altitude with a deserted outflow (shown in Fig. 15 by an arrow); so that one might think it impossible to escape from Dick Lauder's inference, dating from 1818, that the waters responsible for the beaches were lacustrine, not marine. The difficulty, of course, which had to be faced in what may be termed the pre-glacial days of geology, was the complete disappearance of the barriers required by the lake hypothesis. This

Fig. 13 The Parallel Roads of Glen Roy. After A. Geikie

difficulty seemed insuperable to Darwin, and led him to claim a marine origin for the successive beaches, and to suggest that the apparent outlets were in reality straits silted up to the level of the strand-lines. We need not elaborate further. For once Darwin blundered sadly, as he realized in later years.

In his paper, which was presented to the Royal Society early in 1839, Darwin makes many references to Lyell in support of his idea of marine submergence, accompanied, as he thought, by iceberg distribution of erratics. He does, in a footnote, also mention 'recent papers' by Venetz, Charpentier, and Agassiz; but no direction is given to help a reader who might wish to consult them.

The following chapter, introducing glaciers into British geology, supplies the key to Glen Roy and much else besides.

Meanwhile let us recall that in Chapter 8 we have referred to a long, somewhat critical article by Fitton, published in the *Edinburgh Review*, 1839, vol. 69. It is entitled 'Mr Lyell's "Elements of Geology", with Observations on the Progress of the Huttonian Theory of the Earth'. In it Fitton definitely claims that Lyell might have acknowledged his indebtedness to Hutton rather more fully. We have already commented on this issue. Here we need only add that a letter is quoted in Lyell's *Life*, dated 1 August 1839, in which the author defends his treatment of the subject. It deserves careful consideration.

Chapter 12

1840

British Glaciers

The year 1840 is ever memorable in the annals of British geology, for in it belief in the former existence of glaciers in our country established a firm foothold. The discovery reached us through Switzerland; but, strange to say, the first suggestion of the previous great extent of Swiss glaciers originated in Scotland.

Though Hutton knew of glaciers only through the writings of the early Alpinist, de Saussure, and other contemporaries, he included them among the agents of erosion enumerated in his *Theory of the Earth*. He also suggested that they, rather than catastrophic deluges, may have carried 'those great blocks of granite foreign to the place on which they stand', which figure in certain Swiss descriptions. Thus on page 218 of his second volume we find the following:

Let us consider the height of the Alps, in general, to have been much greater than it is at present; and this is a supposition of which we have no reason to suspect the fallacy; for the wasted summits of the mountains attest its truth. There would then have been immense valleys of ice sliding down in all directions towards the lower country, and carrying large blocks of granite to a great distance, where they would be variously deposited, and many of them remain an object of admiration to after ages, conjecturing from whence and how they came. Such are the great blocks of granite which now repose on the hills of *Salève*.

One need scarcely be surprised that, while Hutton offered this suggestion to his Swiss *confrères*, he did not think of applying it in Scotland. Still, he did realize his inability to explain, 'for example, why upon an eminence or the summit of a ridge of land which declines on every side, an immense mass of travelled soil appears'.

Hutton's two most distinguished disciples, Sir James Hall and John Playfair, reacted in very different fashion to his suggestion regarding widespread glaciation of Switzerland in bygone times.

Hall had travelled in Switzerland in his young days, and disagreed with Hutton's explanation of boulder transport by glaciers. He favoured a gigantic wave from the ocean, impelled by an earthquake and capable of detaching ice-bergs to carry erratics from the Alps to the Jura. The idea of using floating ice for boulder-transport he attributed to Wrede, who in 1802 had employed it to account for 'foundling blocks' on the North German plain. (He seems to have overlooked Hutton's suggestion of floating ice for the carrying of boulders across the Swiss Plain—with changed geography but without a deluge.) We have already referred to Hall's use of similar interpretations for a whole group of phenomena in the Edinburgh district. He read his paper on the subject before the Royal Society of Edinburgh, 1812.

Playfair was unconvinced by Hall's arguments, with which he was acquainted long before their publication. It is true that in his *Illustrations of the Huttonian Theory*, 1802, he does little more than repeat, without emphasis, his master's suggestions about the possibility of glacial transport in Switzerland; but as soon as peace had been declared in 1815, though sixty-seven years of age, he went to see, among other matters of interest for his never to be completed second edition, the Mont Blanc granite boulders stranded on the slopes of the Juras. He died in

1819, but his notes, taken on the spot in 1815 (his whole excursion reaching to Naples lasted seventeen months), were published in 1822, in the first volume of his *Collected Works*. They were for the purpose edited by his nephew James G. Playfair, and refer to a particularly large boulder some 2,520 tons in weight:

When we consider that the nearest point where the granite is to be found in its native place is at a distance of 70 miles, it will appear no easy matter to assign a conveyance by which this block could have performed such a journey over intervening hills and valleys without considerable injury. A current of water, however powerful, could never have carried it up an acclivity, but would have deposited it in the first valley it came to, and would in a much less distance have rounded its angles, and given it the shape so characteristic of stones subjected to the action of water. A glacier, which fills up valleys in its course, and which conveys the rocks on its surface free from attrition, is the only agent we now see capable of transporting them to such a distance, without destroying the sharpness of the angles so distinctive of these masses. That mountains formerly existed of magnitude sufficient to give origin to such extensive glaciers, is countenanced by other phenomena observed in the Alps, and does not imply any alteration in the surface, so great as the supposition of a continued declivity between the two extreme points, which is, after all, insufficient to remove the objection arising from the sharp angles of these rocks.

Playfair, as we have seen, came determined to check Hutton's ideas by critical examination in the field. Looking across the great Swiss Plain that separates the Juras from the Alps with the Salève in between, he might well have drawn back in scientific terror at the magnitude of the phenomena that presented themselves for consideration. Instead he not only accepted Hutton's suggestion of a glacier from Mont Blanc to the Salève, but *with good reason* extended it all the way to the Juras. *Also* he realized that the form of the country beneath its icy covering may have been much the same as we see it, uncovered, today.

Again and again we are amazed at the originality of one
who modestly claimed the title of Illustrator!

Fig. 14 Glacial carry from Mt Blanc to Salève and the Juras

The next step in recognition of the former great extent
of Swiss glaciers is marked by a paper read in 1821
(published 1833) at the eighth meeting of the Swiss
Society of Scientists. Its author, an engineer, Ignace
Venetz, pointed to moraines far beyond the present limits
of glaciation in his native country; and in 1829 he went
further, referring the wide distribution of erratics, not
only here, but also in northern Europe, to transport by

Plate 12 The Parallel Roads of Glen Roy.

Plate 13 Floating ice, after Sir James Ross.

Plate 14   The Niagara Falls.

Plate 15   The Agassiz Rock, Blackford Hill, Edinburgh.

glaciers. He made a very important convert in his friend, Jean G. F. de Charpentier (1786–1855), manager of a salt works at Bex, who in 1834 gave an important address at Lucerne on moraines, erratics, and striae. Like Hutton, Charpentier was prepared to account for the former big glaciers by postulating former big mountains—but for the moment we are concerned only with the glaciers, not their cause.

When Venetz and Charpentier realized the glaciers, it was without any prompting from predecessors. All the same, Charpentier, in 1841, generously acknowledged Playfair's priority; and he was able to cite only two other anticipators in the world of science: Goethe, in the 1829 edition of his *Wilhelm Meister*, and Esmarck, of Norway, 1827. He added, however, that many Swiss peasants understood the significance of the erratic blocks and scratched surfaces which they were accustomed to find far beyond the termination of modern glaciers. Since then James David Forbes (after becoming a famous glaciologist) looked up his lecture notes, taken in 1827 in the Natural History Class, Edinburgh, and found that his 'respected teacher and friend, Professor Jameson, even at that time referred to the erratic phenomena in Scotland, as perhaps requiring to be explained by the former presence of glaciers'. Darwin, we may recall, attended some of Jameson's course in 1826, so that he too may have heard this remark, which seems to have borne little if any fruit. We shall return to Jameson in 1840.

It is scarcely surprising that Charpentier should not have traced Playfair's views back to their Huttonian source; but it is a little strange, and certainly amusing, that Archibald Geikie should have failed in this direction: strange, because to Geikie, more than to anyone else since Playfair, belongs the credit for securing wide recognition for Hutton's *Theory of the Earth*; amusing, because in his ex-

K

cellent preface to Volume 3 of the *Theory*, published post-humously, 1899, we find the following statement: 'The two published volumes of the *Theory* have neither an index nor a detailed Table of Contents. . . . I have thought that the index, made by me originally for my own use in studying this classic, may be found of service by others, and it is accordingly appended to the present volume.' It is now obvious that in this quotation 'made by me' means 'made for me', since the index includes page references to: '*Ice, transport of erratics by*'. It is a fair inference that the maker of the index had found Volume 2 of the *Theory* less unreadable than had the author of the *Founders of Geology*; also, that the latter, if he noticed that the index spoke of ice transporting erratics, took it for granted that *ice* here meant *floating ice*.

To begin with, Agassiz had opposed Venetz and Charpentier; but in 1836 he was won over by the latter, and soon came to be considered the outstanding exponent of the subject. In 1840 his classic *Études sur les glaciers de la Suisse* was published. It was dedicated to Venetz and Charpentier, but scarcely does justice to his indebtedness to them. There are many geological features, too, in this fine work which call for criticism; but here let us concentrate on his support of Venetz's view that there has been extensive, fairly recent glaciation of northern Europe.

Prepared to scoff, Buckland in 1838 visited Agassiz at Neuchâtel, and was shown the glacial phenomena in the neighbouring Juras. Not as yet quite convinced, he examined for himself actual glaciers in the Alps. He then returned and told Agassiz (what this scientist already realized) that there was similar evidence in Scotland and England, evidence which he had up to date included in his *Reliquiae Diluvianae*. Buckland persuaded Agassiz to come over in 1840, when the British Association was to meet in Glasgow for the first time. This would give him an

opportunity to confirm British glaciation in the field—
fossil fish were also dangled as an additional bait.

In 1840, true to his promise, Agassiz came. If we turn
to the Transactions of the Geological Section of the British
Association, we gather that at some date between 18 and
23 September Agassiz delivered a paper indicating past
extensive glaciation, not only of Switzerland, but also of
northern Europe, Asia, and America, as set out in his
recently published *Études*.

This in itself might well have furnished Maclaren, the
redoubtable editor of the *Scotsman*, with acceptable news
for comment; but there was much crisper material soon to
follow. Agassiz having joined forces with Buckland, at once
penetrated into the Highlands; and as a result readers of
the *Scotsman* found themselves faced with articles on
glaciers on 7 October, 11 November, 26, 30 December
(1840), and 2, 6, 13, 27 January (1841). These have in
large measure been gathered into Maclaren's *Select
Writings* edited by K. Cox and J. Nicol (1869).

The first article may be regarded as a great journalistic
scoop. Agassiz had found that traces of glaciation, which
he perceived at Glasgow, became increasingly strong as he

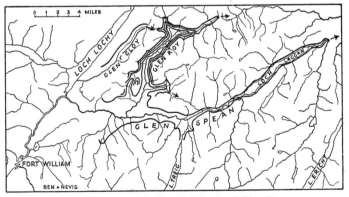

Fig. 15 Map of the Parallel Roads of Glen Roy

advanced into the Highlands. 'The parallel roads of Glen Roy are intimately connected with this former occurrence of glaciers, and have been caused by a glacier from Ben Nevis. This phenomenon must have been precisely analogous to the glacier lakes of the Tyrol, and to the event that took place in the valley of Bagne [Drance of Fig. 6].' So a Swiss geologist had at last reconstructed the vanished barriers that, in conjunction with cols, determined the successive levels of Lake Glen Roy! Here indeed was a matter upon which even non-geologists could form an opinion.

The above information was conveyed in a letter from Agassiz to Jameson, dated Fort Augustus, 3 October; received 6 October; and rushed into the *Scotsman* 7 October. The following quotation from the first of the *Scotsman* articles explains how it happened:

The letter to Professor Jameson was intended to appear in the *Philosophical Journal*, which, however, was published some days ago, and the Professor has obligingly transmitted it to us for insertion in the *Scotsman*, with the following note: 'I enclose an extract of the letter received from Agassiz, dated Fort Augustus, October 3, which has just reached me, but too late for the *Philosophical Journal*. As it is of great importance from a geological point of view, I send it for insertion in your journal. It proves the former existence of glaciers in Scotland, and gives what may be considered the true explanation of the parallel roads of Glen Roy, etc. etc. Ever since I published the account of the great *moraines* in Norway, in districts where no glaciers are now to be seen, I have kept a look-out for further information on this important subject, and have not failed to lay before the public, in the *Edinburgh New Philosophical Journal*, the results of the observations of the most accurate travellers and naturalists on the natural history of glaciers, such as Esmark, Scoresby, Latta, Wahlenberg, Charpentier, Venetz, and, in the late numbers of the *Edinburgh New Philosophical Journal*, also of Studer, Renoir, and, above all, the truly original and beautiful investigations of Agassiz.

The last of the *Scotsman* articles, 27 January 1841, stands away from the others. In it Maclaren reviews the mode of carry responsible for the present positions of some 500 boulders of Salisbury Crag dolerite lying about in Queen's Park, Edinburgh. He took up the matter anew in the hope that glacier transport might afford a clue. Unfortunately he missed the truth because some of the boulders have reached heights well above the outcrop of the dolerite. He could not reconcile this with glacial carry in spite of Agassiz's record of Swiss striae often pointing uphill.

In passing, it may be noted that the best account of Agassiz's glacial work in Britain is in the *Edinburgh New Philosophical Journal*, 1842.

Well before the *Scotsman*'s stream of articles had ceased, three papers had been presented at the Geological Society, London:

4 *November*. Agassiz: Glaciers, and the evidence of their having once existed in Scotland, Ireland and England.

4, 18 *November*. Buckland: Evidences of glaciers in Scotland and the North of England.

18 *November*, 2 *December*. Lyell: Geological evidence of the former existence of glaciers in Forfarshire [Angus].

These three papers present a wonderfully good first attempt at dealing with the glaciation of much of the British Isles. One might have expected that the authors, all of great renown and Buckland actual President of the Society, would have received a respectful, perhaps even sympathetic, hearing, such as had been extended to Agassiz by Jameson and Maclaren in Scotland; especially as they were self-confessed converts. The reverse is true, though the *Proceedings* of the Society give no hint as to what actually happened, because the Society at that time frowned on any record of discussion. Fortunately, however, a subcurator secreted an account which was eventually published in the *Midland Naturalist*, 1883; fortunately, too, H. B. Woodward reprinted it in his splendid *History of the Geological Society of London*, 1907.

The yachtsman naturalist, James Smith of Jordanhill, Glasgow, did indeed remind the audience of the arctic character of some of the shells found in raised marine clays along the Scottish coast, about which he had begun to publish just a year previously; but otherwise all seemed convinced of the absurdity of British glaciers. The talk continued on one occasion to midnight with competition for a place on the floor. For instance, while William Whewell, Master of Trinity, Cambridge, is expounding difficulties, we read:

Mr Lyell — 'I have attempted to account for that in my paper' — here interrupted.

Dr Buckland — 'So have I in a paper which is not yet written!'

Mr Whewell, continuing — 'Our attention tonight is limited to Dr. Buckland's paper'.

In his Presidential Address which followed soon afterwards in February 1841, Buckland reviewed the situation in very conciliatory style. The contest between the adherents of land-ice and sea-ice, he thinks, 'will probably be settled, as in most cases of extreme opinions and exclusive theories, by a compromise; the glacialist will probably abandon his universal covering of ice and snow, and will be content with glaciers on the elevated regions of more southern latitudes than now allow of their formation; the diluvialist, retaining his floating icebergs as the most efficient agents in the transport of drift and erratic blocks to regions distant from their place of origin, may also allow to glaciers their due share in the formation of moraines and striated surfaces, in latitudes and elevations that are no longer within the zones of perpetual congelation'.

Buckland in the above correctly foretold the attitude of average British geologists for the next twenty years. The reaction of the Lyell-Darwin combine seems typical: Lyell in 1841, faced with the erratics and striae of New England, just like those of Sweden, declared them the work of floating ice, *because* there were no mountains in sight to nourish glaciers; while Darwin in 1842 rejoiced to recognize vanished glaciers among the mountains of North Wales, where neither Sedgwick nor himself in 1831 had seen 'a trace of the wonderful phenomena all around'. This was the last field-work that Darwin's health allowed him to undertake.

Lyell in his 1840 paper had argued that his native county of Angus had provided the site for an ice-sheet such as we see today in South Georgia, with 'erratic blocks conveyed almost imperceptibly along the surface of the frozen snow to great distances'. It is probable that for several years to come he may sometimes have regretted this paper as an indiscretion. At any rate he was very reticent on the subject. We may, for instance, compare the 1840 sixth edition of his *Principles*, published before Agassiz's visit, with his 1847 seventh edition. The most significant change is a passing reference to 'what has been termed a glacial epoch'. Still, in the interval, in the second edition of his *Elements*, 1841, he admits 'the probable existence of glaciers . . . when erratics were dispersed from the Grampians'; and he discusses as quite possible Agassiz's theory of the Parallel Roads of Glen Roy.

Lyell's 1850 (eighth) and 1853 (ninth) editions of the *Principles* are a little more forthcoming than the seventh; and, as we shall see in Chapter 19, in 1857 he banished his remaining doubts.

Let us note in passing that a lot of what Lyell says in

his various publications regarding dispersal of erratics by icebergs, shore-ice and river-ice is both true and interesting. Floating ice (as also seaweed) has helped to re-arrange many of the boulders along our shores, and at one time or another floating ice has dropped numberless boulders on to the floor of the sea—James Smith's bedded, arctic, marine clays furnish plenty of examples. Lyell, however, was wrong in attributing a whole series of land-glaciation phenomena to this agency, for instance: un-bedded boulder clay with most of its material derived from the immediately underlying formation; and harmonious striation often running across the grain of the country, uphill and down dale, aligned with crag and tail and with drumlins.

As regards the sea-shells that are locally found in drift, their distribution often proclaims glacier-carry rather than submergence, for again and again shelly drift extends on to higher ground than is occupied by non-shelly drift just alongside.

The above criteria can be applied only after a considerable area has been examined. Sometimes, however, evidence proving land-glaciation is presented, as it were, in a nutshell. At Blackford Hill, Edinburgh, there is a shallow grotto, in what is now called the Agassiz Rock (Pl. 15). In the autumn of 1840, Maclaren led Agassiz to examine it. 'The rock leans forward, forming a sort of a vault. The surface of the clinkstone, for the space of ten or twelve feet in length, is smoothed, and marked by *striae* or scratches in a direction approximating to horizontal. . . . Agassiz instantly exclaimed, "That is the work of the ice".' By ice he meant glacier-ice, which could mould itself to an overhanging surface, a feat that no one would claim for the ice of an iceberg.

Still the fight between sea-rovers and land-lubbers continued as a perennial feature of British Association meetings till about 1902. In that year Percy Fry Kendall demonstrated widespread temporary diversion of British rivers by glaciers during succéssive stages of the Great Ice Age. It was a repetition of the Glen Roy story, but with emphasis laid on eroded spillways rather than on lake terraces.

Chapter 13

First Visit to America – Interval

The years 1841-2 were dominated for Lyell by a thirteen-month trip which he undertook with his wife to North America. This adventure was based on an invitation to give a course of lectures at the Lowell Institute in Boston. Its story is recorded in a small two-volume book, *Travels in America*, published in 1845, and in some score of scientific papers. Before starting, Lyell had seen a second edition of his *Elements* appear, in June 1841.

His travel-book is written mainly in the form of a journal, and one might be tempted to regard it as inspired by a desire to recover expenses, which may not have been wholly met out of lecture fees. Probably, however, its real origin lay in an almost irrepressible desire to tell a traveller's tale. Thus on 12 October 1842, we find Lyell writing as follows to a congenial spirit in Boston, the historian George Ticknor, to whom eventually he dedicated his volumes: 'Yet, I cannot bear not to take the opportunity, not only of telling my friends what route I took and how long I tarried, that they may test my opportunities of observation—but also of saying how I liked and what I thought of the people and country, as I ran through it on a railway, or the deck of a steamer.'

Lyell and his wife left from Liverpool on 20 July 1841, and arrived back at the same port, with three dozen boxes of specimens on 27 August 1842. They wandered up and down, and to and fro, from the Atlantic to Lake Erie, and from Lake Ontario and the St Lawrence to Cincinnati and Charleston. They travelled mostly by rail, steamboat, and locally-hired carriage; and they generally stayed at inns,

Fig. 16 Travels in North America

though sometimes they accepted private hospitality, especially in the South. They had an exceedingly kind and helpful reception, with geological guidance on many occasions; but they were hard at it most of the time with hammer or pen, and had to refuse a multitude of invitations.

In the following brief outline the subject matter is regrouped more or less in accordance with its place in geological time.

The North furnished splendid exposures of fossiliferous Early Palaeozoic sediments. At Quebec these can be seen resting unconformably on old crystallines. At Niagara they have determined the nature of the great falls. At the latter locality Lyell had the invaluable guidance of James Hall of New York.

In Nova Scotia, with the experts Abraham Gesner and John William Dawson, Lyell visited the Joggins sections of Coal Measures at the Bay of Fundy. These are famous for upright casts of tree trunks standing perpendicular to inclined bedding. It had so happened that in June 1839 and February 1840 three papers had been read at the London Geological Society favouring the growth-in-place theory of coal production. Two concerned casts of tree trunks in the Manchester coalfield, entirely comparable with those of Joggins; while the third, by William E. Logan, announced that seat-earths with *Stigmaria* underlie upward of a hundred coal seams in South Wales: the *Stigmaria* Logan interpreted as roots. It was a great pleasure for Lyell to examine a repetition of these phenomena at Joggins. He was also able to extend Logan's stigmarian observation to the Pennsylvanian coalfield, no matter whether the coals there were bituminous or anthracitic—as they become where involved in the folding and incipient metamorphism of the Appalachian chain. Lyell was in Nova Scotia long enough to correct a general impression that the gypsiferous formation associated with the Coal Measures is of New Red age. He found it underlying, not overlying, the Coal Measures; and he interpreted it as Lower Carboniferous. (Before the Lyells left America, Logan had arrived to start, in 1842, the Geological Survey of Canada.)

In the Appalachians Lyell had most helpful guidance in the field from Professor Henry Darwin Rogers of Pennsylvania. Later, in April 1842, he attended at Boston the third meeting of the Association of American Geologists, when H. D., with his brother William Barton of Virginia, made the Appalachian chain world-famous by vivid description of its folds. These structures naturally recalled to Lyell folding he had already seen on the Berwickshire coast and again in the Jura Mountains. In his *Elements* he had told how Sir James Hall of Scotland had in 1812 attributed such folding to lateral compression, and had imitated it experimentally. Lyell himself, however, had reserved judgment. As for the Jura folds, we know that Thurmann, at the time he showed the arches to Lyell, ascribed each to independent uplift. Now the brothers Rogers claimed that 'the wave-like flexures of our Appalachian chain are the results of an onward, billowy movement proceeding from beneath, and not of a folding due simply to some great horizontal or lateral compression'. Lyell having seen all three folded belts seems to have favoured something approaching Thurmann's outlook (abandoned later, 1857, by its author). 'I cannot', says Lyell, 'imagine any real connection between the great parallel undulations of the rocks and the real waves of a subjacent ocean of molten matter on which the bent and broken crust may once have rested. . . . The uplifting movements may be propagated along narrow belts, and may have been in progress simultaneously, or in succession in one narrow zone after another. . . . The failure of support arising from subterranean causes may enable the force of gravity, though originally exerted vertically, to bend and squeeze the rocks as if they had been subjected to lateral pressure.' There seems a muddle here; but it is probably fair to clarify it by suggesting that Lyell rejects the Rogers' waves and also Hall's conception of lateral compression due to intrusion of granite somewhere out of sight; and instead accepts confusedly the popular notion of lateral compression as a by-product of subsidence. In the second volume of his *Travels* he makes a point of the present-day elevation of the Appalachians being independent of the conspicuous folding, since the folds were for a time buried under New Red Sandstone, still approximately flat.

The Mesozoics and Tertiaries south of New Jersey were of special interest to Lyell; but here we may pass on to what is now called Pleistocene. Lyell was much impressed by the erratic formation and underlying striae, conspicuous from New York northwards, and absent farther south. We have already seen that he attributed the erratics and striae to floating ice, because he thought that glaciers need mountain support. The parallelism of striae over large areas led him to picture ice-floes, miles in extent. He was disappointed not to find striae along the St Lawrence attributable to river-ice. He did indeed find a very few striae on soft sandstone at the Bay of Fundy, which must have been caused by drifting shore-ice; but they seemed very poor compared with the Pleistocene scratches on granite and schist.

Whenever Lyell heard of a mastodon or elephant he made a beeline for the site; but he learnt little about these animals beyond the fact that they had inhabited North America along with modern molluscs.

In 1839 James Smith of Jordanhill, Glasgow, had, as already noted, announced to the Geological Society of London his discovery of arctic sea-shells in the older raised beach deposits of the Clyde. At the same meeting Lyell had given an account of similar shells sent him by Captain Bayfield, R.N., from a raised beach near Quebec. In both cases the fauna was very close to that gathered previously by Lyell at Uddevalla, Sweden (Fig. 11). Naturally Lyell followed up this point on the ground, making many observations and collections; but the raised beaches of the St Lawrence and the Great Lakes are a complex subject.

The arctic faunas mentioned above belong to Late Glacial times, and are more alike on the two sides of the Atlantic than are the coastal shells of today. Still Lyell was surprised, rather than otherwise, to find that about a third of present-day temperate shells seemed identical, though separated by this ocean. The birds and plants are much more distinct. Lyell was astonished to realize that minute humming birds migrate seasonally from Florida to Niagara and Nova Scotia, and back again. He also found the total absence of the heath family very striking; and he learnt with interest that attempts to coax the common daisy of England to grow on American lawns had all ended in failure.

Two features of present-day physical geography made a specially deep impression, namely, the Great Dismal Swamp of Virginia and North Carolina, and the falls and gorge of Niagara. The swamp Lyell took to be a coal-seam in the making; the falls he interpreted, in company with previous observers, as parental to the gorge.

Lyell employs as frontispiece of the first volume of his *Travels* an idealized bird's-eye sketch reaching from Queenston upstream to Lake Erie, with the gorge and falls in between (Pl. 17); and into this he has introduced the various geological formations that had been named for him by Hall. The original sketch had been given to Lyell by the son of the Bakewell whose book long ago had introduced him to geology. Young Bakewell in 1830 had published a discussion of Niagara in *London's Magazine*; and, like certain others, had calculated how long it must have taken the falls to cut the seven-mile gorge between it and the Queenston escarpment. Lyell points out that the variables are too important to justify the attempt.

Instead, Lyell concentrated on a demonstration that the river really had cut the gorge, which he did by tracing river deposits at plateau level margining the gorge for some miles downstream from the falls. This may seem superfluous; but it must be realized that Lyell at this stage of his career still greatly underestimated the potency of subaerial erosion in shaping scenery. For him the Queenston escarpment, from which the gorge starts, was an old sea-cliff, in the production of which marine erosion, during slow upheaval of the land through the zone of breakers, had accepted guidance from geological structure—and if the great escarpment represents an old sea-cliff, why should not the gorge be a narrow strait excavated in advance? One is reminded of his treatment of Weald erosion in Volume 3 of the *Principles*! (But see later in Chapter 19.)

Let us now turn from rocks and natural history to mankind; and let us group a few notes regarding the human reactions of the Lyells, taking them geographically from north to south. The British possessions visited by the Lyells were Upper Canada (Ontario), Lower Canada (Quebec), New Brunswick, and Nova Scotia. The two Canadas, English and French in origin, had mounted rebellions as recently as 1837; and these had been backed by sympathizers from New York State armed with cannon looted from State arsenals. As a consequence British regiments were a prominent feature; but the British parliament, although it had hurriedly recalled the conciliatory Governor, the Earl of Durham, was already acting on his famous *Report* of 1839. Thus in 1840 it united the two Canadas with a view to eventual combination of all British possessions in North America to become a self-governing dominion.

One thing that struck Lyell forcibly, quite apart from British-French contrasts, was the greater vitality that

Plate 16
An erratic on a glacier.

Plate 17
Niagara. A diagrammatic
sketch by Bakewell Jun.
and Lyell, showing
Queenston in the fore-
ground, the Falls in the
middle distance, and Lake
Erie in the background.

Plate 18   The Great Dismal Swamp.

appeared in towns of the United States, no matter how short a distance they lay south of the border. This he attributed to the reluctance of settlers from New England to make their homes in British-owned territories. A similar reluctance was shown by these same settlers to enter the slave states of the Union, where manual labour was not regarded as a proper white man's burden.

The readiness of New Englanders to invest money in education impressed Lyell very favourably. He noted that Boston was spending £30,000 a year on public instruction within the city boundaries—as much as England set aside for the same object within its national frontiers. This he considered 'is the only good result which I could discover tending to counterbalance the enormous preponderance of evil arising in the United States from so near an approach to universal suffrage'. As he saw it, it was a case of the rich educating the poor in the hope of improving their votes. His own prescription was to establish a means test for voters, and to disqualify immigrants until they were thoroughly assimilated.

Lyell was well pleased with the fees he received from the Lowell Institute. This literary and scientific foundation had been endowed with £70,000 by a wealthy Bostonian, John Lowell, who died in 1836; and a condition had been laid down that no money was to be spent on building. Though the lectures were to be free, tickets had to be applied for some weeks in advance. Even so Lyell found he had to give his lectures in duplicate to keep the audience down to about 1,500 at a sitting. The fees were more than three times higher than were awarded to the best public lecturers in London. The anti-building clause in the will stirred Lyell to enthusiasm. Half a million sterling had been bequeathed by Girard to found an educational institution at Philadelphia with the express desire that the architectural ornament be kept moderate. 'It is doubtful',

L

says Lyell, 'whether the remaining funds will suffice for the completion of the palace—splendid indeed, but extremely ill-fitted for a schoolhouse!' He then thinks of the money spent on building University College and King's College at home in London, and groans aloud. Lyell also gave lecture courses at New York and Philadelphia, thus materially helping his travelling account.

He was greatly pleased by the religious side of public education in New England. There were plenty of sects, and not a little ill-feeling; but the great majority agreed that no one sect among them should be given a privileged position. 'The Bible is allowed to be read in all, and is actually read in nearly all the schools; but the law prohibits the use of books calculated to favour the tenets of any particular sect of Christians. . . . In New York the Roman Catholic priests have recently agitated with no small success for a separate allotment of their share of the education fund. . . . But there is no reason to apprehend that any one sect in New England will have power to play the same game.'

While in this mood Lyell devoted a long discussion to the inferiority of Oxford and Cambridge to the universities of the United States. Most of the professors at Oxford and Cambridge were Anglican clergy; the degree subjects were restricted to mathematics and classics; degrees were only given to Anglican students; the time-table was so arranged that it was practically impossible for students to attend lectures other than those on degree-subjects. The universities had become 'places for educating the clergy of the Established Church, and the aristocratic portion of the laity professing the same form of Christianity'. The 'sufficient counter-poise' suggested is a Royal Commission.

In Philadelphia, 1842, the closing of certain banks disposed of most of the paper money the Lyells carried. It was a hard time for many citizens of the United States, and for many more in the British Isles, since various states (outside New England) defaulted. This emphasized very clearly, Lyell thought, the danger of unrestricted suffrage. The states in question could have continued to pay interest if their electorates had been prepared to pay special taxes for the purpose; but their electorates were not prepared for the associated sacrifice.

Still, though ready to find fault on occasion, Lyell and Mrs Lyell felt themselves on the whole in splendid company, building roads, railways, and steamers, pushing out to the West, familiar in address, man to man, genuinely respectful, man to woman—of whatever social standing.

The Lyells wintered, geologizing, in the South, where they met the very difficult problem of slavery. The English, we must remember, had played the major part in conducting the appalling transatlantic slave traffic. Organized protest had first come from Quakers of Pennsylvania and the homeland. By 1804 both England and the United States had outlawed the slave-trade for their nationals; and in 1838 all slaves in the British West Indies had been liberated with compensation paid to owners. By this time too a majority of states in the Union had no-slavery laws, starting with Vermont in 1777.

'The negroes', says Lyell, 'so far as I have seen them, whether in domestic service or on the farms, appear very cheerful and free from care, better fed than a large part of the labouring class of Europe; and, though meanly dressed, and often in patched garments, never scantily clothed for the climate. We asked a woman in Georgia, whether she was a slave of a family of our acquaintance. She replied, merrily, "Yes, I belong to them, and they belong to me". She was, in fact, born and brought up on the estate.'

And again: 'Had the measure of emancipating all the slaves been carried through as rapidly as some abolitionists have desired, the fate of the negroes might have been almost as deplorable as that of the aboriginal Indians.'

Lyell, however, is deeply shocked to hear that marriage among the slaves has 'no legal validity' (so as not to complicate individual sale), and that it is unlawful to teach a slave to read and write (for fear of spreading ideas of freedom). He thinks that the planters in their own interest should educate their slaves (so as to be worthy freemen when the time comes), and that they should encourage individual liberation (thus preparing the way for general emancipation).

In his letter to Ticknor, from which we have already quoted, Lyell makes his position doubly clear: 'When I was with the planters', he says, 'seeing their kindness to their slaves, and feeling that, had I inherited their estates, I should not well know what to do; I could not but feel that a London emancipation meeting, or a list of advertisements by Dickens, raked out of newspapers from all parts, would irritate and indispose me to exert myself in forwarding the cause of emancipation. Sydney Smith said to me one day: "But you should hold up the system to the reprobation of mankind." I replied that it must be a work of time, sacrifices must be made and the philanthropists ought to share them with the planters.'

Dickens has just been mentioned. Writing in Philadelphia Lyell tells how: 'The newspapers are filled with accounts of the enthusiastic reception which Mr Charles Dickens is meeting with everywhere. Such homage has never been paid to any foreigner since Lafayette visited the States. . . . There may be no precedent in Great Britain for a whole people thus unreservedly indulging their feelings of admiration for a favourite author; but if so, the Americans deserve the more credit for obeying their warm impulses.'

After arriving back at Liverpool in August 1842, the Lyells made their way to Kinnordy before returning for the winter to their home in London. Meanwhile, the Darwins migrated to Down, which, combined with Darwin's habitual ill health, diminished considerably the close contact of the two friends.

Next year Lyell toured Auvergne (Fig. 9), seeing a 'wonderful collection of mammalia, of one hundred and sixty-five extinct species of all periods from the eocene to the pliocene, which the Abbé Jean Baptiste Croizet and Auguste Bravard have disinterred from the old freshwater marls and the volcanic alluviums, etc., of all ages'.

He then, with Mrs Lyell, attended a British Association meeting at Cork, and proceeded by Killarney and the Giant's Causeway (Fig. 1) to Scotland once again. The Cork meeting was not very enthusiastic, with O'Connell's agitation for repeal of the Union attracting more local attention than the discoveries of science. Still, Lord Rosse, President for the year, had already a great telescope with which he had achieved 'grand results'. In passing we may note that Lyell never evinced much sympathy with the Irish peasantry, apparently thinking that refusal to pay rent while starving showed lack of public spirit, or else, perhaps, a too expensive spiritual ransom paid to Rome.

In 1844 Lyell went to York for the next British Association gathering; and later in the year, on the request of Prime Minister Peel, he co-operated with Faraday in supplying a *Report* on a disastrous explosion at Haswell Colliery, Durham. Many years later (1868) Lyell recounts that Faraday inquired at the site of the explosion how they measured the air current in the mine. One of the men took a pinch of gunpowder from a box and dribbled it down on to a candle flame, and timed the travel of the smoke. Faraday then asked where they kept their store of powder. 'They said they kept it in a bag, the neck of which was tied up tight. "But where", said he, "do you keep the bag?" "You are sitting on it" was the reply; for they had given this soft and yielding seat as the most comfortable one at hand to the commissioner. He sprang upon his feet in a most animated and impressive style, . . .'

In 1845 we find Lyell interceding on behalf of Agassiz for an allotment of a course of Lowell lectures, which was successfully arranged for the following year. The matter had been raised by Agassiz after he had been offered an allowance by the King of Prussia, activated by Humboldt, to help him on his way. (The canton of Neuchâtel, Fig. 6, since 1815 had belonged to the Swiss Federation, but was unique in being also a principality which owed some measure of allegiance to the King of Prussia.) Mrs Lyell, acting as secretary, gave, on 28 February, an encouraging reply: 'My husband thinks your plan a very good one, and sure to succeed, for the Americans are fond of that kind of instruction. We remember your English was pleasant, and if you have been practising since, you have probably gained facility in expression, and a little foreign accent would be no drawback. . . . In six weeks you might earn enough for a twelve months' tour, besides passing an agreeable time at Boston, where there are several eminent naturalists.'

At this time the Lyells must have been planning their second visit to the United States—without lecture commitments. At any rate, off they started on 4 September 1845.

Chapter 14

1842-1844

Darwin and Chambers

We shall rejoin the two Lyells on their second American trip in the following chapter. Meanwhile let us turn aside to consider stages in Darwin's biological education, which were destined profoundly to influence Lyell's subsequent career. In Chapter 10 we have seen how in 1837 Darwin started a notebook on *Transmutation of Species*. Fifteen months later, in October 1838, he turned for amusement to Thomas Robert Malthus' *Essay on the Principle of Population* (probably the sixth edition, 1826; the first appeared in 1798). Familiar with 'the struggle for existence which everywhere goes on', he had in 1837 already jotted down that adaptation leads to survival and nonadaptation to extinction. Still Malthus' *Essay*, with its arithmetical treatment, seems to have stirred him as never before. 'Here then', he exclaims in his Autobiography, 'I had at last got a theory by which to work': that 'favourable variations would tend to be preserved, and unfavourable ones to be destroyed'. This idea of natural selection he developed sufficiently to write in June 1842, shortly before leaving London for Down, a pencil sketch of his species theory.

The sketch of 1842 was expanded very considerably in 1844; and, in an accompanying letter to his wife, Darwin explained that he would like it published if he should die before a more elaborate statement had been completed.

In regard to editors, who were to receive £400 to £500, he said: 'Lyell, especially with the aid of Hooker (and of any good zoological aid), would be the best of all'; but ten years later he added: 'Hooker by far the best man to edit my species volume. August 1854.'

The change of choice probably resulted from Darwin's finding Joseph Hooker much more receptive of his species ideas, and more interested in his experiments on the dispersal of seeds. We learn that the 1844 copy 'was read by Dr Hooker, and its contents afterwards communicated to Sir Charles Lyell'. It is natural to suppose that Darwin felt some delicacy in pressing home his arguments upon the latter, who had conspicuously identified himself with the conception of fixity of species.

By strange coincidence the year 1844 saw also a quite independent step taken towards the establishment of the evolutionary interpretation of the living world. With this intention a book was published in London entitled *Vestiges of the Natural History of Creation*. At first the author chose to be anonymous; but in later editions he acknowledged that he was Robert Chambers of W. and R. Chambers, Publishers, Edinburgh.

Robert Chambers (1802-71) was a little senior to Darwin, and started his studies early. In after life he recalls that: 'Books, not playthings, filled my hands in childhood. At 12 I was deep, not in poetry and fiction, but in encyclopaedias.' It is not surprising that eventually he and his brother William produced the well known *Chambers's Encyclopaedia* (1859-68) which still appears in revised editions.

Meanwhile Robert Chambers supplemented his wide reading with field research in geology; and he soon became sufficiently known in scientific circles to render his attempted anonymity only nominal.

Chambers's *Vestiges* starts with an account of cosmical

evolution largely based on an encyclopaedic article by John Herschel—but with passing reference also to Laplace. Chambers concludes that this evolution is a fact, and that it has been guided from the beginning by natural laws laid down by 'a First Cause . . . a primitive almighty will'. Thus astronomy predisposed Chambers to interpret the development of the organic world in terms of natural laws, very much as Lyell's uniformitarian geology predisposed Darwin in the same direction.

Chambers accepted, along with almost all geologists, the idea of *progress* in the fossil record (for Lyell's alternative turn back to Chapter 8). He also accepted Lamarck's claim that existing forms have evolved from pre-existing forms—instead of being introduced as new creations. His acknowledgment, scarcely exuberant, runs as follows: 'Early in this century a naturalist of the highest character, suggested an hypothesis of organic progress which deservedly incurred much ridicule although it contained a glimmer of the truth.' Having said so much (and one must remember that Lamarck's views were at the time intensely unpopular) Chambers hastened to dissociate himself from his predecessor's attempts to locate the *cause* of the changes which both agreed to have occurred.

Lamarck thought, in regard to animals at least, that hereditable changes have followed from efforts of creatures to take fuller advantage of their environment.

Chambers, dismissing this idea as ridiculous, referred change to a natural law that a living creature faced with a new or altered environment will (under certain circumstances predestined by the First Cause) mutate to take advantage of the new situation.

It is difficult to see that Chambers's view of continuity, determined by Natural Law, has much advantage over non-Lamarckian discontinuity determined by repeated creations; but Chambers points out that it would save the Creator a great deal of trouble, especially as He would presumably have an infinite number of habitable globes to supervise.

While there is in modern eyes 'a glimmer of the truth' in much of Chambers's book, one must admit that the good is plentifully mixed with bad. This is particularly the case in relation to its Chapter 15, entitled the *Maclean System of Animated Nature*, which elaborates a farcical classification of the animal world. The reception among babes and sucklings was enthusiastic, and among the scribes and pharisees of science correspondingly bitter. Sedgwick, the following year, 1845, after consulting Herschel, Agassiz, Owen, and Clark, wrote a long, ferocious criticism for the *Edinburgh Review*. His object, as he explained in a letter to Lyell, was 'to strip off the outer covering and show its inner deformity and foulness'.

Darwin also wrote to Lyell, in this case regarding the review: 'Nevertheless, it is a grand piece of argument against mutability of species, and I read it with fear and trembling.'

Later after reading the tenth (1853) edition, Darwin gives the following considered opinion: 'The work, from its powerful and brilliant style, though displaying in the earlier editions little accurate knowledge and a great want of scientific caution, immediately had a very wide circulation. In my opinion it has done excellent service in this country in calling attention to the subject, in removing prejudice, and in thus preparing the ground for the reception of analogous views.'

Chapter 15

1845-1846

Second Visit to America

In a two-volume book, *A Second Visit to the United States of North America*, published in 1849, Lyell narrates his and Mrs Lyell's experiences on a journey, starting from Liverpool on 4 September 1845 and returning on 13 June 1846. The three years' delay in publication was largely due to a determination to give precedence to scientific results set out in scientific journals. Most of the papers dealt with coalfields of Carboniferous or, at James River, Mesozoic age. One of them furnished an account of footprints 'allied to cheirothereum' which Lyell had been shown in Pennsylvania. The book, when it did appear, was much more colloquial than that describing the first visit, and contained relatively little of what Sydney Smith disparagingly called 'Lyell's Greywacke'. It passed through three editions between 1849 and 1855.

Concerning the old consolidated rocks, the book's main features of interest are confirmation of the presence of toed quadrupedal footprints in true Pennsylvanian Coal Measures, fifty kilometres east-southeast of Pittsburgh (Fig. 16); and of the Jurassic age of the Richmond, or James River, coalfield in Virginia. Lyell's account of his work at Richmond in the *Journal of the Geological Society* is supplemented by a description of fossil plants which he had brought home with him. This and much other co-operation in later years he owed to Charles J. F. Bunbury,

who in 1844 had married Frances, second daughter of
Leonard Horner.

Comparatively very recent deposits attracted Lyell to

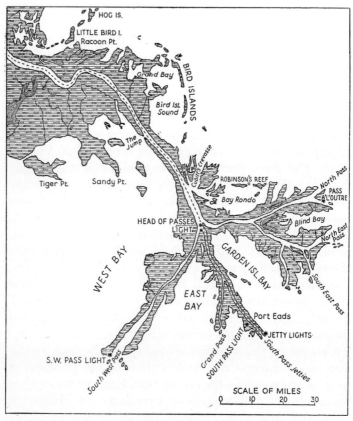

Fig. 17 Mississippi delta

localities in Georgia and Mississippi, where northern
mastodons had met with southern megatheriums, both
treading down molluscan species that persist today. Lyell's
identification of the loess of the Mississippi basin as a

counterpart of that bordering the Rhine is also note-
worthy, though he still regarded the deposit as essentially
fluviatile rather than in large measure windborne. His
remarks on the Mississippi River, more than a hundred
feet deep and escaping into the sea by levée-bordered
distributaries, across bars with only sixteen feet of clear-
ance, are equally arresting. Finally, most important of all
is his investigation of the testimony preserved in landscape
and human memory of the terrible earthquakes of New
Madrid, Missouri, 1811-12. The disturbance was of unusual persistence. Humboldt had already remarked 'that
the shocks of New Madrid were the only examples on
record, of the ground having quaked almost incessantly
for three months, at a point so far remote from any active
volcano'; and Lyell repeats stories of how the country
people, having noted that fissures generally opened in a
particular direction in any one locality, felled tall trees at
right angles to this direction to serve as refuges in times
of spasm.

Lyell devotes much of his human commentary to advantages to be expected from education and religious
tolerance. He has, however, to admit disappointment at
the wide credence given in well-educated New England
to one, Miller, who foretold that the world would end on
23 October 1844. As for the prevailing religious tolerance,
he traces it back in large measure to reaction against the
Calvinism of the early Puritans. He was given a copy of
a poem of 224 stanzas called the *Day of Doom*, which the
children of certain schools, seventy years previously, had
had to learn by rote. From his quotations we may select
the following:

Poet: Then to the bar all they drew near
                Who died in infancy,
             And never had, or good or bad,
                Effected personally.

Infants: Not we, but he, ate of the tree
    Whose fruit was interdicted;
   Yet on us all, of his sad fall,
    The punishment's inflicted.

Judge: But what you call old Adam's fall,
    And only his trespass,
   You call amiss to call it his,
    Both his and yours it was.

Poet: The glorious King, thus answering,
    They cease, and plead no longer,
   Their consciences must needs confess
    His reasons are the stronger.

   God's vengeance feeds the flame
   With piles of wood and brimstone flood,
   That none can quench the same.

On slavery Lyell maintained his former moderate views aimed at education and eventual liberation. He and Mrs Lyell always went to church, black or white, on Sunday; and they were often favourably impressed. They found too that many missionaries taught slaves to read the Bible, though this was illegal; and that public opinion discouraged the splitting of families, though in law no families existed. On the other hand they shrank from the results of drunkenness, rife among planters; and were offended by the markets and advertisements, where slaves figured as mere biped cattle. A subsequent letter, dated 30 October 1852, expresses Lyell's feelings very clearly: '*Uncle Tom's Cabin* will, I hope, do more good than harm on the whole. It is a gross caricature, because the very great number of kind masters, and of families where the same negroes remain for generations, is carefully kept out of view. But all the evils described, or nearly all, do now and then occur in a population of nearly four millions. As to Congress it can no more interfere constitutionally than our Government to reform the harems and other abominations in Turkey.' (*Uncle Tom's Cabin* was published in America in 1852. By February 1853 Lyell learnt that over a million copies had been sold in England—presumably pirated. At the time his own publisher, Murray, was seriously considering a five thousand issue for the forthcoming ninth edition of his *Principles*.)

At first Lyell was thrilled with the river steamers of the South, but after winding for hundreds of miles up the Mississippi he began to be bored. He even tired of the familiarity of fellow passengers who soon peered through the monocle suspended from his neck. However, he concluded: 'to one who is studying the geology of the valley of the Mississippi, the society of such companions may be endurable for a few weeks'.

Moreover, only on one occasion did he find cause to retreat from his opinion formed in 1841-2 that, in America, a man never shows disrespect to a woman. He tells the story with a smile. Here it is:

A New Haven coach starts with the Lyells as its sole inside passengers. *En voyage* it picks up two respectably dressed young men and young women, who bargain for inside places at reduced fare. Their manners and conversation cause offence to Mrs Lyell. The coach changes horses. Lyell complains. The coachman takes the young men aloft. The young women sit demure for half a mile and then burst into uncontrollable laughter. They hear rain pelting down on outside passengers.

It so happened that relations between Britain and the United States were very strained during the Lyells' 1845-6 visit, though this does not seem to have detracted from the friendly personal welcome the couple everywhere received. In 1839 the 49th parallel had been accepted as the boundary between British and United States' possessions from the Lake of the Woods, on the west margin of Figure 16, all the way to the Rocky Mountains. Beyond this to the sea a provisional arrangement gave both powers a share in administration. At first the country concerned was mainly of interest to British trading companies, who had a near-palaeolithic sympathy with Indians, bears, and musquash; but by 1842 settlers began to arrive from the United States by the Oregon Trail with a much more neolithic outlook, seeking clearings and crops. The United States' government of 1846 was very bellicose, claiming all the Pacific coast between Russian Alaska and Mexican California. Lyell found it an anti-climax to turn from the American press, largely preaching war, to the British papers, brought by mail-boat and much more concerned with repeal of the Corn Laws than with quarrels abroad. Before the end of 1846 a treaty was signed, less generous to trappers than to settlers, but still securing for the former, and for the future Dominion of Canada, Vancouver and Vancouver Island.

In 1845, admission of Texas, mostly west of the area shown in Figure 16, to statedom in the U.S.A. soon led to even bigger expansions of the latter. Texas entered the Union as a slave-state, and the Lyells saw many families of 'movers' with their slaves and other possessions trekking thither from the east. The resultant accession of strength to the slave-owning states as a whole greatly annoyed the no-slave states farther north, and led to many a struggle for position in years to come. Adoption of Texas also precipitated war with Mexico, who had not accepted the secession of this territory in 1835. The result, reached eventually in 1848, was an enormous extension of the Union's territories covering country since allotted to California, Nevada, Utah, Arizona, and New Mexico, altogether west of the area shown in Figure 16.

On their return to London the Lyells moved for more ample accommodation into 11 Harley Street, long previously occupied by Sir Arthur Wellesley, now Duke of

Wellington; and in September we find Lyell telling the British Association at Southampton some of his American adventures. There he met his friend Agassiz talking of London Clay fishes on his way to Boston. With Edward Forbes to help, Lyell thought that he had on this occasion pretty well convinced Agassiz that some of the Crag molluscs are identical with living species. Agassiz, like many others, was, and continued to be, a believer in wholesale replacement of faunas at the start of each geological formation.

M

Chapter 16

1846-1853

Revolution – Knighthood – Exhibition

During the winter, 1846-7, dinner parties in a select circle were much enjoyed. Here literature with history and biography had pride of place. Lyell's strictures on Oxford and Cambridge set out in his *Travels in America* got a wonderfully sympathetic hearing; and he writes: 'Nothing, I find, surprises our University men so much as to learn, *inter alia*, that whereas under Roman Catholic rule the principal teachers of academical youth married and settled at Oxford and Cambridge, all those who now really and efficiently engross the educational function are enjoined to celibacy.' There can be little doubt that Lyell's outspoken condemnation played a considerable part in the struggle for reform, which in 1858 got as far as to permit Dissenters to enter for the B.A. Meanwhile, Whewell, Master of Trinity, in 1847 prepared a scheme of reform for Cambridge; but at the same time he wrote Lyell a private 'letter of remonstrance'. Lyell replied, and received an answer which was 'quite a knock-under as to every disputed fact, and extremely pacific'. 'A petition', writes Lyell in 1848, 'is getting up for a royal commission to go to Oxford and Cambridge, and the signatures of fellows of colleges, and even of the clergy, are already most numerous.'

Lyell attended the British Association at Oxford in June 1847. There was a goodly company who were greatly amused by son Buckland, now a student of Christchurch. Following his father's tradition he had dressed a young bear in cap and gown, and was introducing him to the eminent visitors. Ruskin was Secretary of the Geological Section.

Sunday 27 February 1848 proved for Lyell a memorable date. He was one of a distinguished party dining with Sir Robert Peel—no longer Prime Minister. Bunsen, Prussian Ambassador (not the chemist), was called upon by his host to give an account of how a member of his staff had escaped from Paris over the barricades of revolution the previous Thursday. 'Bunsen told us that there are some 30,000 communists in Paris who are for property in common and no marriage.'

It was the end of Louis-Philippe's reign, which had started in 1830 during Lyell's visit to the volcanoes of Olot. The junior Bourbon had come to the throne as a reformer, but had steadily moved over to despotism, and had consistently refused appeals to widen the franchise.

The result in France was the short-lived Second Republic, soon manoeuvred by Louis Napoleon into the Second Empire, 1851-70. The result in Europe outside of France was the Year of Revolutions. In the Canton of Neuchâtel, for instance, a republican uprising ousted the King of Prussia, thus incidentally interrupting Agassiz's scientific allowance. A new Chair of Zoology and Geology was offered to him at Harvard, which he accepted. His clear recognition that the glaciation of the northern States and Canada was the work of land-ice contributed to early widespread adoption of this interpretation. We may add that Lyell does not seem to have borne him any consequential ill will.

Another feature of 1848 was the election of a new President of the Royal Society following the Marquess of Northampton, who in 1838 had succeeded the Duke of

Sussex. Lyell supported De la Beche in favouring a scientific, rather than aristocratic, president, and a term of office restricted to two years. No decision was reached in Council beyond deputing Edward Sabine and Lyell to approach Sir John Herschel to ask him to stand once again as a candidate. In the end, with Herschel, Faraday, and Robert Brown all refusing, the Earl of Rosse agreed to accept the office.

Knighthood. Still another event of 1848: in September Lyell received a letter from Lord Lansdowne (Lord President of Council) telling how he had recommended him for the honour of knighthood, and how he had Her Majesty's 'authority to state that she will most willingly confer it upon you, and that she understands that it is without any solicitation on your part'. So, from Kinnordy Lyell rode over the hills by Clova and Lochnagar to Balmoral, and received the accolade at Her Majesty's hands. The first letter of congratulation that reached Lyell from outside the family circle came from his old friend Mantell.

Great Exhibition. From this time forward Lyell saw a good deal of the Prince Consort, during very occasional visits to Balmoral and Osborne, but more especially in connection with the Great Exhibition of 1851, in regard to which he served as a Royal Commissioner for Life. We can judge from his private correspondence that he shared with other distinguished geologists, including De la Beche, Murchison, and Sedgwick, a genuine admiration for the Prince's advanced views concerning science, art, industry and education. Similar appreciation does not seem to have been widely entertained by non-scientific contemporaries.

Elected once more President of the Geological Society, February 1849, Lyell secured the attendance at the inaugural dinner of the Archbishop of Canterbury, Sir Robert Peel, 'and a great many M.P.'s and notabilities', so that the speaking was 'the most brilliant we ever had at any anniversary. Sedgwick spoke most eloquently, and Peel; and the Archbishop made a straightforward and manly speech'.

The corresponding Presidential Address followed in a year's time, February 1850. By chance it fell to Lyell's lot to pronounce an obituary on Christian VIII of Denmark, who had been a fellow of the Society since 1822. This was the same Christian who, as Crown Prince, had extended help and encouragement to Lyell in his early days of Scandinavian research. The Address itself was rather disappointing. Its main object was to demonstrate that there is no need to postulate greater activity of earth-movement in Tertiary times than today. Amid a cloud of hypothesis it is a relief to find him pointing out that, at any rate, the erratic formation should no longer provoke a fiction of sudden uplift.

At the succeeding Anniversary, February 1851, Lyell had the pleasant task of presenting Adam Sedgwick with the Wollaston Medal and Joachim Barrande (*in absentia*) with the Wollaston Fund, received for transmission by Foreign Secretary Bunbury. Death had dealt hardly with the Society during the past year, and the loss of Peel and Northampton among others was properly noted. The Address this time was palaeontological. Transmutation theories, Lyell reminds his audience, 'I have uniformly opposed, for twenty years, and the favour which they have acquired of late, with the general public, in consequence of the eloquent pleading of the anonymous author of the "Vestiges of Creation", has been more than counterbalanced by the refutation which it has called forth in the writings of Owen, Sedgwick, and Hugh Miller'. So far, so good; but these three great men were Progressionists, and Lyell was not. Broadly speaking the Progressionists regarded both extinction and creation of species as First Cause phenomena, aimed at *progress*. Lyell, on the other hand, considered the appearance of progress, enshrined in the palaeontological record, to be a mere illusion based upon the imperfection of the record. For him extinction was determined by Second or Natural Causes connected with Natural Changes in environment. Creation he did invoke as a First Cause operation; but its aim, he thought, was *adaptation* to changed environment. The extinguished organism was adapted to the environment of yesterday; the created organism to that of today. 'There is change, but can you call it progress?'

Man, Lyell holds in this Address to be a very late creation (later than the extinction of the mammoth). He stands widely separate from other animals. Accordingly 'the creation of man would seem to have been the beginning of some new and different order of things', and must not be claimed as an example of progress.

A quite distinct part of Lyell's 1851 Address was devoted to the close juxtaposition of Coal Measure plants and Liassic shells at Petit-Coeur near Moutiers in the Alps. Lyell had in a previous Presidential Address (1837) urged a tectonic explanation; but Murchison and others had since accepted de Beaumont's interpretations that here Coal Measure plants had survived into Liassic times. Lyell strengthened his previous position, which has since gained universal acceptance.

Meanwhile, on 8 November 1849, Lyell's father had died at the age of eighty-two. His mother survived into the following year after retiring with her daughters to the dower house. The main Kinnordy house and the estate were let.

In 1850 the Lyells spent August in Belgium and Germany learning in their usual fashion more of the geology

and geologists. It was pleasant to meet at Potsdam
(Fig. 10) with Humboldt once again. Early in our story
it was pointed out that Lyell, wherever he went, sought
out the local geologists with the same zest as he searched
for exposures. In previously unvisited country he often
carried letters of introduction, but failing these he would
make insistent inquiries, holding that every village includes
a naturalist; and he never forgot Murchison's advice to
start asking at the chemist's shop.

Publication and the coming Exhibition occupied much
of Lyell's time. In 1851, before the opening, he writes to
Ticknor: 'The Prince Consort is a host in himself in forwarding education, worth all the English Whigs put
together. Oxford and Puseyism, and Evangelism and a
State Church and the narrowness of excluded sectarianism,
are fearful odds against us.' He then passes on to bewail
Louis Napoleon and his Praetorian Guard and Jesuits.

The Exhibition opened on 1 May and proved, as all
know, a triumphant success. Lowell, cousin of the founder
of the Lowell Institute at Boston, was an early visitor;
and he took the chance to arrange for Lyell to give a
second course of lectures in the autumn of 1852. This
involved a third trip to America; but before it materialized,
Lyell served on an Oxford University Commission, which
produced what he himself called 'a really grand report'.

Lady Lyell accompanied her husband to America (Fig.
16); and the excursion, starting in August, lasted at any
rate into November. Its most important scientific result
was a joint paper by Lyell and Dawson on a quadruped
and land-shells in the Carboniferous rocks of Nova Scotia,
1853. The shells are nowadays called *Pupa vetusta*.

A fourth and final trip across the Atlantic arose directly
from the Great Exhibition. The Government wished to pay
a compliment to a New York Industrial Exhibition to be
held in 1853, and asked Lord Ellesmere and Lyell to

represent their goodwill. Lord Ellesmere had 'really great knowledge and taste in the fine arts', while Lyell was a man of science and 'one who would be acceptable to the American people'. The whole business occupied about two months, and followed the publication of the ninth edition of the *Principles*.

Chapter 17

Further Travels – Ancient Man

1853-7 Fossils and Glaciers Galore

The winter of 1853 found Lyell and his Lady, together with Mr and Mrs Bunbury, setting sail for the volcanoes of Madeira, whence, at the start of 1854, they passed on to those of the Canary Islands. They returned home in April. By this time the initial stages of the Crimean War had started, with Britain allied to Louis Napoleon. In the autumn the Lyells removed to 53 Harley Street.

In 1855, and again in 1856, the Lyells geologized in Germany (Fig. 10). In the latter year they greatly extended their trip to include Vienna and Switzerland. At Prague they were fortunate to meet Joachim Barrande, eighty-seven years old, but, says Lyell, 'just what I knew him [in Paris and London] thirty years ago'.

Let us continue with a further quotation:

[This wonderful Frenchman] was tutor to the Duc de Bordeaux formerly, and is now Chief manager of his estates. When Charles X [after the 1830 revolution] went into exile to Prague in 1832, Barrande settled there, and finding the Germans were neglecting the older (Silurian and Cambrian) rocks, and that these were rich in fossils, he set to work, and spent all his own private fortune in opening and operating quarries expressly for the fossils. How many thousand pounds sterling he expended in twenty-four years I cannot say; but he told me in order to explain the eighteen metamorphoses of a trilobite called *Sao hirsuta*, he collected 20,000 specimens, and they cost 5,000 francs, or

£200. He has at length got 1,500 species, and nearly all of them are peculiar to Bohemia, or new. He showed me these in his museum. . . . He explained to me on the spot his remarkable discovery of a 'colony' of Upper Silurian [Silurian] fossils 3,408 feet deep, in the midst of the Lower Silurian [Ordovician] group. This has made a great noise.

Lyell in rather muddled fashion thought he could improve upon Barrande's colonization theory, whereas in essence he merely repeated it in other words. The true explanation is that the stratigraphical succession has been misleadingly shuffled by earth movement.

At Tübingen, Lyell found Quenstedt, 'a hard-working, enthusiastic, and original man. Like Barrande, he has opened large quarries in the lias and oolite exclusively for fossils.'

At Zürich, he was shown by Oswald Heer fine collections of fossil plants; but what struck him most was a superb collection of Miocene insects from Oeningen, among which were 30,000 species of beetles alone!

Altogether Lyell was metaphorically feasted.

Swiss Glaciation. The next excursion was made in 1857, and was mainly devoted to a scrutiny of the evidence which had led Swiss geologists to attribute the wholesale glaciation of their country to land-ice, rather than sea-ice. The result was a very great advance in Lyell's understanding of the subject. He was completely satisfied with the land-ice interpretation. His judgment was based upon close comparison of the ancient and modern natural records of glaciation. He admits, however, that he was influenced by the ever present view of snow-clad Alps, and by the complete absence of sea-shells from the drifts of the country.

Lyell's conscience was now made easy on the score of his 1840 paper on glaciers in Angus. The Highlands, he felt, might well have played in the glacial epoch the part of the Alps, and the Sidlaws that of the Juras (Figs. 8, 14). At the same time he retained sea-ice for the glaciation of much of England and North America. In this he was mainly mistaken.

Across the Alps on the Italian side he was on sure ground again (Figs. 6, 9). 'The ancient mighty glacier derived from the combined snows of the Mont Blanc and Monte Rosa group of Alpine heights . . . has certainly left, as [Bartolommeo] Gastaldi first pointed out in a memoir on the subject in the French Bulletin, a far more imposing monument of itself on the plains of the Po than have the extinct glaciers of the Rhône or the Rhine in the lower country of Switzerland.'

In this 1857 exploration, and on previous occasions, Lyell received generous guidance from Escher von der Linth and Studer, who as close, though free, companions laid the broad foundations of Swiss geology. These two have been likened to Peach and Horne, Investigator Twins of later date in Scotland; but another comparison concerns us here, due to the great international tectonist, Eduard Suess of Vienna, who chose to contrast Escher with his contemporary Lyell, as exemplifying the wide scope of geological allegiance. The following is taken from the preface to the English version of Suess's masterpiece, *The Face of the Earth*:

In 1854 I became acquainted in Switzerland with Bernhard Studer and Escher von der Linth. Escher with all his simplicity was a remarkable man. He was one of those possessed with the penetrating eye, which is able to distinguish with precision, amidst all the variety of a mountain landscape, the main lines of its structure. He had just come forward with the magnificent conception, unheard of in the views of that time, of a double folding of certain parts of the Alps, which has since received the name of the 'double fold of Glarus'. Studer opposed him. Such movements of the mountains were, he said, contrary to nature and inexplicable. Escher did not concern himself with the explanation, but with the facts.

A few years later I had the good fortune to make the acquaintance of Sir Charles Lyell, with whom, as with Escher, I maintained friendly relations till the close of his life. On the one side stood Sir Charles, the calm superior philosopher, the lucid thinker and clear writer; and on the other dear old Arnold Escher, who entrusted his admirable sketches and diaries to every one indiscriminately, but to whom every line he had to publish was a torment, and who was perhaps only quite in his element up in the snow and ice, when the wind swept his grey head and his eye roamed over a sea of peaks. In characterizing this time I only mention these two important men, because in the contrast of their qualities the whole field of activity in our glorious science is brought into view.

(Perhaps a word of explanation is required here. Suess knew when he wrote the above that the double fold interpretation of Glarus was wrong in an essential feature, but this did not blind him to the large measure of truth which it enshrined.)

1857-9 Volcanoes – Copley Medal – Ancient Man

The 1857 excursion, which we have been following in the previous chapter, was continued to Naples and Sicily to allow Lyell to restudy Vesuvius and Etna. Adherents of von Buch and de Beaumont had affirmed that lavas which congeal on a declivity exceeding 5° or 6° are never continuous or solid, but are entirely composed of scoriaceous or fragmentary material; and they had accordingly interpreted steeper dips of stony layers, found in the cones of all the great central volcanoes of the world, as proof of upheaval about so-called 'craters of elevation'. Lyell, on the other hand, had always backed up-building rather than upheaval of volcanic cones. Now, at typical exposures of historic lavas on the slopes of Etna, he saw a number of stony cores with moderate to steep dips, sometimes surpassing 40°. This and other volcanic features he described in a paper read to the Royal Society, June 1858; but he

Fig. 18 Etna lava consolidated on a steep slope. A. Upper part of the road called the Scalazza; B. Bastione del Toco; C. Lava-current which descends the cliff to the Grotto delle Palombe; D. Grotto delle Palombe.

reserved full publication in the *Philosophical Transactions* (vol. 148), 1859 (see Fig. 18). His final illustrated account, including additions based on still another trip to Sicily in 1858, reads quite convincingly.

By this time Lyell was sixty-one years old, but, leaving Lady Lyell with relations in Germany, and with mules and guides to help, he made the summit of Etna and slept four nights in a shelter, Casa Inglese, at 10,000 feet. 'It is extraordinary', he wrote to one of his sisters, 'how one comes through it all with health and spirits. I must say it often did me good to think how our officers fared in the Crimea, and under an Indian sun, to say nothing of being shot at to boot.'

Although not shot at, Lyell in 1858 received a very distinguished award, the Copley Medal of the Royal Society. In the citation he was hailed as a leader in almost every branch of geology. Hutton and Playfair are mentioned as forerunners—probably at his own suggestion.

In his Italian trips Lyell took a sympathetic interest in the awakened nationalism of that divided country. He also welcomed recent excavation of classical antiquities in Rome. In the religious field, he was amused at a former French ambassador having made a splendid collection of Tertiary fossils in the hill of the Vatican with a view to publication; for this contrasted strongly with the fact that no lectures on geology were authorized in the Sapienza. The English sculptor, Gibson, was less fortunate than the French ambassador. He wanted an account of his allegorical sculptures, which accompany his statue of Wellington, to be printed in an Italian periodical; but the censor struck out the description of an angel carrying the Duke's soul up to heaven, as this was impossible, seeing that the great man lived and died a heretic.

Since the triumphal Newcastle meeting of 1838, Lyell had often attended the British Association, and on a number of occasions had been President of the Geological Section. In 1859 at Aberdeen he held this post again, and it was a very special occasion since the Prince Consort officiated as President-in-Chief. 'The Prince's speech', we are told, 'was well delivered.' Not unnaturally it now makes dull reading, though its tribute to von Humboldt, recently deceased, must have recalled to Lyell early days in Paris.

'I had thought it best', Lyell writes to his mother-in-law concerning his own Sectional Address, 'not to ask the Prince to be there, though I had two talks with him at Banchory. But next morning Sabine came with a message that H.R.H. the President requested me to defer my opening speech till he could attend at 12 o'clock, so I got Prof. Nichol [Nicol] first, on the "Geology of Aberdeen-shire". When the Prince came, the room, which had been gradually filling, must have contained about 800. The

Prince, the evening before, had 2,200 and many ladies had been refused tickets.'

'Young [Archibald] Geikie has read the best paper to my mind yet presented to our section, on the "Age of the various Trap Rocks of Scotland". He finished by endeavouring to prove the top of Arthur's Seat to be Tertiary! Of the young men he is certainly the coming geologist and writer. I am glad Horner likes his book [*The Story of a Boulder*, 1858]. I expect he will one day be a leader in the Ordnance Survey.'

The main feature of Lyell's Sectional Address was acceptance of man as contemporary with the mammoth. In this he reversed the opinion which he had expressed in his 1851 Presidential Address to the Geological Society. The tide had turned, and was now carrying him forward from the anchorage of prejudice and caution where, for a time, he had sought shelter. Some of the main circumstances are outlined below.

At least three British records dating from the eighteenth century recall finds of human bones or artefacts in close association with the remains of extinct mammals such as the mammoth. One of these, by John Frere, 1797, concerned a discovery in undisturbed clay at Hoxne in Suffolk, and definitely suggested that the artefacts there present belong 'to a very remote period indeed; even beyond that of the present world'.

Turning to Belgium, we find that from about 1830 P. C. Schmerling had diligently collected bones and flint implements from virgin caves near Liége. He obtained bones and artefacts of man, which he claimed to be obviously contemporaneous with abundant remains of extinct mammals. As we have seen in Chapter 9 Lyell visited Schmerling in 1833 and found his evidence 'far more difficult to get over than any I have previously heard of'.

In 1825, Boucher de Perthes at the age of thirty-seven succeeded to his father's post as Director of Customs at Abbeville on the Somme. Next year he noticed flints of unusual form in a neighbouring gravel pit. By 1832 he had satisfied himself that these had been shaped by man, although they would have to be as old as the containing gravel which yielded many bones of extinct animals.

Fig. 19 Paleolithic flint implement from the Somme

Boucher's views, set out in lectures to the local *Société d'Émulation*, and next year to the Paris Institute, were received with incredulity. A book followed, but without effect. At last one of his critics, Dr Rigollot of Amiens, began to dig for himself, and, to his surprise, repeated Boucher's experience. Rigollot published in 1854.

Returning to 1825, we find a Roman Catholic priest, John MacEnery, starting to investigate Kent's Hole near Torquay (Fig. 1). Soon he recognized flint implements definitely associated with remains of extinct mammals. He died in 1841 leaving a manuscript stating his results. This remained unpublished until (abridged) it appeared in 1859. MacEnery seems to have refrained from declaring his convictions out of deference to Buckland. The latter, along with most other authorities, thought that originally separate deposits had somehow been subsequently mixed. Two important investigators, Robert A. C. Godwin-

Plate 19 Earth pillars at Bolzano in the South Tyrol.

Plate 20 Earth pillars, drawn by Herschel.

Plate 21   The river Mole breaching a chalk escarpment just south of a large quarry.   The river flows away to the left.

Plate 22   The Märjelensee, Switzerland.

Austen and William Pengelly, maintained that MacEnery had not been deceived; but they did not command attention until a virgin cave at Millhill, Brixham, also in the neighbourhood of Torquay, was discovered in 1858.

The Royal Society and public-spirited individuals provided funds; and a committee of geologists was established to supervise the investigation of this Millhill cave. The best-known members of the committee were Hugh Falconer, the great authority on fossil elephants, and Joseph Prestwich, specially versed in the Tertiaries and Quaternaries of the South of England; but the actual conduct of the operation lay in the hands of Pengelly. By 1859, when Pengelly conducted Lyell through the excavations, the contemporaneity of man and his extinct companions was fully established.

The same year Falconer, on his way to Sicily, called on Boucher, and was greatly impressed with his collection. Accordingly he wrote to Prestwich advising him to make a careful investigation of the Somme field-evidence. This Prestwich was speedily able to do along with John Evans, and the two of them were completely satisfied. Lyell in his Address puts it thus: 'For a clear statement of the facts, I may refer you to the abstract of Mr. Prestwich's memoir in the Proceedings of the Royal Society for 1859, and have only to add that I have myself obtained abundance of flint implements (some of which are laid upon the table) during a short visit to Amiens and Abbeville.'

There was a sad sequel, which Lyell was not able to foresee, a sequel with a Piltdown flavour. From 1860 workmen began to salt Boucher's pits with faked hand axes and in one case with a human jawbone.

Here let us pass on to another very significant item in Lyell's Address. It reads:

That the doctrine of progressive development may contain in it the germs of a true theory, I am far from denying. The con-

N

sideration of this question will come before you when the age of
the White Sandstone of Elgin is discussed—a rock hitherto referred to the Old Red, or Devonian formation, but now ascertained to contain several reptilian forms, of so high an organization as to raise a doubt in the minds of many geologists whether
so old a place in the series can correctly be assigned to it.

A few more words are perhaps required, after a hundred
years, to recall the interest of this once hotly debated topic.
Recognition of the reptilian nature of fossils in the Elgin
Sandstone dates back to 1850. The sandstone repeats
Upper Old Red Sandstone characters and rests concord-
antly on Upper Old Red Sandstone richly charged with
typical Upper Old Red Sandstone fish. It was, therefore,
claimed by many as belonging itself to the Upper Old Red
Sandstone formation. Thomas Henry Huxley, however,
protested strongly. The following enumeration will show
how in the end the battle went.

In December 1858 Murchison read a paper to the
Geological Society supporting the Old Red Sandstone
solution.

In a postscript dated June 1859 he stated that on
Huxley's advice 'it becomes me to pause in my geological
conclusions', and to obtain new evidence 'before the ensuing meeting of the British Association at Aberdeen'.

During the meeting Robert Harkness and John Miller
both voted for Old Red Sandstone.

After the meeting Lyell, William S. Symonds, William
Jardine, Harkness and Lord Enniskillin visited the exposures; and Symonds spent some days on them. His
verdict was New Red Sandstone.

In an insert dated January 1860, accompanying the
postscript quoted above, Murchison groups the Elgin
Sandstone as Trias??, 'having', as he says, 'throughout my
geological career invariably bowed to the weight of
palaeontological evidence'.

In a letter dated October 1860, Lyell throws in an aside regarding Elgin: 'I abandon the Old Red reptile, which will gratify the progressionists.'

Finally, let us quote from Lyell's Address the following as furnishing a preview of Darwin's eagerly awaited *Origin of Species*:

Among the problems of high theoretical interest which the recent progress of Geology and Natural History have brought into notice, no one is more prominent, and at the same time more obscure, than that relating to the origin of species. On this difficult and mysterious subject a work will very shortly appear, by Mr. Charles Darwin, the result of twenty years of observation and experiments in Zoology, Botany, and Geology, by which he has been led to the conclusion, that those powers of nature which give rise to races and permanent varieties in animals and plants, are the same as those which, in much longer periods, produce species, and, in a still longer series of ages, give rise to differences of generic rank. He appears to me to have succeeded, by his investigations and reasonings, in throwing a flood of light on many classes of phenomena connected with the affinities, geographical distribution, and geological succession of organic beings, for which no other hypothesis has been able, or even attempted, to account.

Chapter 18

Origin of Species

Let us recall how Darwin, after opening in 1837 a first notebook on *Transmutation of Species*, prepared rough drafts in 1842 and 1844 before sitting down to write a detailed book on the subject. The 1844 draft was read, as we have already seen in Chapter 14, by Joseph Hooker, and afterwards its contents were communicated to Lyell. Probably the latter revolted from close examination of what he sadly thought involved a deplorable departure from the true doctrine of the fixity of species.

For a time Darwin had much on his hands besides the building up of his theory of the origin of species. In 1845 he published the second edition of his *Journal of Researches*, and in 1846 the last of his geological books, *Geological Observations on South America*. From then onwards to 1854 he was engrossed in monographing barnacles, ancient and modern. Probably during these and following years he would speak to Lyell of his species ideas, but with little encouragement. Since he was determined to go very deliberately towards the eventual publication of his theory it seems surprising that he did not put out a preliminary note with promise of more to follow. Such a move would have obviated embarrassment of fellow workers, some of whom knew vaguely what was hatching at Down and must have felt called upon not to trespass. Though Darwin made no preliminary announcement until well nigh forced, we know that he was understandably keen not to be anticipated. Under all these circumstances one might have expected strict secrecy; but the following quotations from letters suggest that few precautions were taken in this matter:

Lyell to Bunbury, 13 November 1854. I have been intending from day to day to write to thank you for your former letter, in which you gave me an account of the conversion of the Aegilops into wheat, which I shall keep for the next edition of the 'Principles'. Hooker seems to believe it, though in general not so prone as Lindley to entertain such ideas.

When we were at Charles Darwin's we talked over this and other like matters, and Hooker astonished me by an account of an orchidaceous plant. . . . You probably know all about this, which will figure in C. Darwin's book on 'Species', with many other 'ugly facts', as Hooker, clinging like me to the orthodox faith, calls these and other abnormal vagaries.

Lyell to Bunbury, 30 April 1856. When Huxley, Hooker, and Wollaston [nephew of W. H. Wollaston] were at Darwin's, last week, they (all four of them) ran a tilt against species farther I believe than they are deliberately prepared to go. Wollaston least unorthodox. I cannot easily see how they can go so far, and not embrace the whole Lamarckian doctrine. . . . Darwin finds, among his fifteen varieties of the common pigeon, three good genera and about fifteen good species according to the received mode of species and genus-making of the best ornithologists, and the bony skeleton varying with the rest!

After all, did we not come from an Ourang, seeing that man is of the Old World, and not from the American type of anthropomorphous mammals? [This last sentence is of course to be taken as a joke.]

Lyell to Hooker, 25 July 1856. Whether Darwin persuades you and me to renounce our faith in species (when geological epochs are considered) or not, I foresee that many will go over to the indefinite modifiability doctrine.

The last two quotations date from 1856. In this year

Lyell persuaded Darwin to pull himself together and make a serious beginning at his projected book. So Darwin started off planning a huge tome, which was destined never to be finished. In the early summer of 1858 he received from Alfred Russel Wallace (1823-1913), writing in the Malay archipelago, a note which unknowingly embodied his own treasured theory of evolution through Natural Selection!

It was a crushing blow for Darwin, but he reacted to it nobly as may be judged from the following letter quoted from Francis Darwin's life of his father, 1902.

Charles Darwin to Charles Lyell
18th June 1858

My dear Lyell — Some year or so ago you recommended me to read a paper by Wallace in the *Annals*, which had interested you, and as I was writing to him, I knew this would please him much, so I told him. He has today sent me the enclosed and asked me to forward it to you. It seems to me well worth reading. Your words have come true with a vengeance—that I should be forestalled. You said this, when I explained to you here very briefly my views on Natural Selection depending on the struggle for existence. I never saw a more striking coincidence; if Wallace had my M.S. written out in 1842, he could not have made a better short abstract! Even his terms now stand as heads of my chapters. Please return the M.S., which he does not say he wishes me to publish, but I shall, of course, at once write and offer to send to any journal. So all my originality, whatever it may amount to, will be smashed, though my book, if it will ever have any value, will not be deteriorated; as all the labour consists in the application of the theory.

I hope you will approve of Wallace's sketch, that I may tell him what you say.

As all know, this very difficult situation was handled with consummate skill. A joint communication by Darwin and Wallace, entitled *On the tendency of Species to form Varieties and on the Perpetuation of Varieties and Species by*

Natural Means of Selection, was read at the Linnean Society on 1 July 1858—with neither of the authors present. An introduction by Lyell and Hooker explained that Darwin's contribution was not prepared for the occasion, but was quoted from: (1) Darwin's 1844 manuscript, read at that date by Hooker, and (2) a letter from Darwin to America's leading botanist, Professor Asa Gray of Boston. This letter was dated October 1857 and served to show that the views expressed in 1844 had not changed in the interval. As for Wallace's contribution the introduction explains:

> This was written in Ternate 1858, for the perusal of his friend and correspondent Mr. Darwin, and sent to him with the expressed wish that it should be forwarded to Sir Charles Lyell, if Mr. Darwin thought it sufficiently novel and interesting. So highly did Mr. Darwin appreciate the value of the views therein set forth, that he proposed, in a letter to Sir Charles Lyell, to obtain Mr. Wallace's consent to allow the Essay to be published as soon as possible. Of this step we highly approved, provided Mr. Darwin did not withhold from the public, as he was strongly inclined to do (in favour of Mr. Wallace), the memoir which he himself had written on the same subject, and which, as before stated, one of us perused in 1844, and the contents of which we had both of us been privy to for many years.

The 1858 dual announcement passed almost unnoticed. The furore awaited the publication in book form next year of Darwin's *Origin of Species,* rushed out by its author as a forerunner of the exhaustive treatise which never materialized. Great support was immediately rendered by Hooker; but Lyell still hesitated. Darwin was deeply distressed to find in his friend's *Antiquity of Man,* which appeared in 1863, no stronger advocacy of the mutability of species than a sentence beginning: 'if it should ever be rendered highly probable that species change by variation and natural selection . . .'. After confiding this much to

Hooker, Darwin continues: 'The Lyells are coming here on Sunday evening to stay till Wednesday. I dread it, but I must say how much disappointed I am that he hasn't spoken out on species, still less on man.'

Poor Lyell! He could only explain to Hooker: 'I have spoken out to the full extent of my present convictions, and even beyond my state of feeling'; and to Darwin: 'I find myself after reasoning through a whole chapter in favour of man's coming from the animals, relapsing to my old views whenever I read again a few pages of the "Principles", or yearn for fossil types of intermediate grade.'

Still, in 1865, Lyell was able to write to Darwin as follows about an after-dinner speech he had just made regarding the award to his invalid friend of the Royal Society's Copley Medal—which, we may note in passing, was given for Darwin's contributions to science other than his theory of evolution: 'I have some note of it', Lyell says in his letter, 'and hope one day to run over it with you, especially as it was somewhat a confession of faith as to the "Origin". I said I had been forced to give up my old faith without thoroughly seeing my way to a new one. But I think you would have been satisfied with the length I went.'

All the same, warm speech is different from cold print. In the tenth edition of the *Principles*, 1867-8 (the ninth had appeared in 1853), we find once more a full and valuable statement of the Darwinian Theory that reads like the summing up of an impartial judge, rather than the declaration of a convert. Two last quotations probably express precisely Lyell's convictions and feelings. The first comes from an 1868 letter to Ernst Haeckel. In this Lyell thanks Haeckel for 'pointing out how clearly I advocated a law of continuity even in the organic world'; but, he adds, 'it remained for Darwin to accumulate proof that there is no break between the incoming and outgoing species, that they are the work of evolution, and not of special creation'. The second is found in a letter to Darwin and is dated 1869. Here we find Lyell expressing himself as not opposed to Wallace's idea 'that the Supreme intelligence might possibly direct variation in a way analagous to that in which even the limited powers of man might guide it in selection, as in the case of the breeder and horticulturist'.

Darwin's ascription of the origin of species to natural causes has seemed to Huxley and other good judges an almost inevitable sequel to Lyell's advocacy of uniformitarianism. Lyell speaking of geology had claimed that one of his main objects was 'to free the science from Moses'. Admittedly later he was frightened of losing all touch with Jehovah if he followed Darwin to what seemed to him the bitter end; but the following quotation from a letter to Ticknor dated January 1860 shows that he was still animated by the old spirit:

I confess that Agassiz's last work [*An Essay on Classification*, 1859] drove me far over into Darwin's camp, or the Lamarckian view, for when he attributed the origin of every race of man to an independent starting point, or act of creation, and not satisfied with that, created whole 'nations' at a time, every individual out of 'earth, air, and water' as Hooker styles it, the miracles really became to me so much in the way of S. Antonio of Padua, or the Spanish saint whose name I forget, that I could not help thinking Lamarck must be right, for the rejection of his system had led to such license in the cutting of knots.

Chapter 19

1860-1875

Closing Down

Two historical events that followed soon after the publication of the *Origin of Species* affected Lyell more closely than the majority of his associates. The American Civil War (1861-5) broke out in April 1861, while the Prince Consort died in December of the same year.

The war provided the *Origin* with a political application. Men asked themselves whether Agassiz was right in supposing that the Black and White races had started as separate creations, or alternatively whether Darwin was correct in regarding them as descended from a common stock.

Lyell was a strong champion of the North. He thought the preservation of the Union and the containment of slavery were in themselves justifiable grounds for fighting. When, later, emancipation was added to these two objectives, he was still more emphatic. He was bitter in regard to the support which the British aristocracy extended to the South, attributing it to prejudice, jealousy, and ignorance, the latter fostered by 'years of insolent and malignant writing by such papers as the *Times* and *Saturday Review*'. This did not prevent him from admiring the pluck of the South in their gallant struggle.

The Prince's death evoked repetition of expressions of high regard such as we have met in earlier letters:

He was always thinking of what could be done to improve the

nation morally and socially, and in the fine arts, and how popular education, and that of the higher classes, could be advanced. . . . He had no special acquaintance with geology or mineralogy, or so far as I know, with any branch of natural history, but he knew enough of all to be interested in them, and to understand what their cultivators were about. How much he desired to encourage them, and how he wished that the elements of these branches of knowledge should enter more largely into the system of education in this country, is well known to all.

Small wonder that such sentiments should prompt Queen Victoria early in 1863 to summon him to Osborne and talk alone with him for an hour and a quarter.

About this time Lyell was offered a Trusteeship of the British Museum, Presidency of the Royal Society, and nomination as a candidate to represent London University in Parliament. All these distractions he refused, 'resolved that he would devote himself to the end of his life to his favourite science, which was daily opening up more interesting matter for study and research'. His attitude in this matter recalls the advice he gave to Darwin in 1836. He could not even spare the five days necessary to receive an Honorary Degree from Edinburgh University; but in 1862 he was elected a Corresponding Member of the Institute of France; in 1863 was given the Prussian Order of Scientific Merit; in 1864 the Presidency of the British Association at Bath; also a Baronetcy; and in 1866 the Wollaston Medal of the Geological Society.

Well-nigh to the end Lyell continued his geological excursions both at home and abroad, and also his attendances at British Association meetings. His main objects were: the publication of his *Antiquity of Man*, three editions in 1863 and a fourth in 1873; a sixth edition of his *Elements*, 1865; and tenth and eleventh of his *Principles*, 1868, 1872. There was also his *Student's Elements of Geology*, in two editions, 1871, 1874.

Two companions now helped Lyell greatly: his nephew Leonard, son of Henry and Katherine, proved a keen comrade in the field; while for his last ten years Miss Arabella Buckley acted as a very efficient secretary, thus offsetting to some extent the progressive failure of his eyesight. Leonard must have been a prodigy, for in 1857, when six years old, we find him in receipt of a letter from his uncle about *Actinia mesembryanthemum*. We are much less surprised to read in an 1865 letter from Lyell to Herschel: 'I took my eldest nephew [Leonard], now aged fifteen, with me on my last expedition to Switzerland and the Tyrol, which added greatly to our pleasure, for he is quite an enthusiast in geology, conchology, chemistry and mineralogy.' As for Miss Buckley, she acquired an extensive knowledge of geology and published three books about it for the benefit of young people.

Many of Lyell's trips were to sites connected with ancient man; though the main interest of the 1865 trip, when he had Lady Lyell as well as Leonard with him, was to compare earth pillars at various localities, and to visit the Märjelensee, impounded by the Aletsch Glacier. Lyell was completely satisfied in both cases. One result was Plate 2 of the tenth edition of the *Principles*, based upon a camera lucida drawing by Herschel, made in 1824 (Pl. 20). It represents a particularly striking group of pillars in the Tyrol, and illustrates valley as opposed to mere gorge erosion. Another was welcome satisfaction that the phenomena of the Märjelensee vindicate Agassiz's 1840 interpretation of the Parallel Roads of Glen Roy (Pls. 12, 22).

We have already noted how Lyell, much to his credit, modified his views as time went on regarding major issues connected with atolls, Swiss glaciation, fixity of species, and antiquity of man. One of his latest enlightenments concerned the vital importance of subaerial erosion in developing scenery. To understand this matter entails a digression.

In 1862 Joseph Beete Jukes, Director of the Geological Survey for Ireland, published a famous classic analysing river development in the neighbourhood of Cork. The region concerned is composed of parallel ridges of Old Red Sandstone separated by hollows dug out in more easily erodable Carboniferous limestone and slate. Jukes argued that the surface at one stage had been smoothed by marine erosion; that it had then been raised with a tilt at right angles to the strike; that streams started flowing down the slope (transverse streams in relation to the strike); that tributaries developed along the outcrops of the more yielding Carboniferous rocks (longitudinal streams); that one or other of these longitudinal tributaries would on occasions cut back thus beheading a neighbouring transverse stream; and so the tendency would be to concentrate stream courses on the yielding outcrops and reduce the crossing of the more resistant Old Red Sandstone to a minimum.

Jukes, assisted by accurate maps, was in reality happily extending views stored up in the writings of Guettard, Desmarest, and Hutton, and at a later date Scrope—not to mention Colonel G. Greenwood, author in 1857 (second edition, 1866) of *Rain and Rivers or Hutton and Playfair against Lyell and All Comers*. It suffices here to quote two of Hutton's dicta: 'We must conclude at least that all the valleys are the operation of running water in the course of time. If this is granted we have but to consider the mountains as formed by the hollowing out of the valleys.' And 'The height of the mountain depends upon the solidity and strength of the stone.' Lyell, when he thought that a transverse stream needed a previous fissure to enable it to pass through an obstacle such as an escarpment, saw in his mind's eye the form of the ground much as it is today, not as it was yesterday when no escarpment had as yet developed.

Andrew Crombie Ramsay, Director of the Geological Survey for Great Britain, speedily adapted Jukes' ideas to explain the river pattern of the Weald (see Pl. 21); but for a time Lyell stood out against him. The difference of opinion is clearly stated in Chapters 6, 18, and 19 of the 1865 edition of Lyell's *Elements*, where we may read such sentences as:

Many of the earlier geologists, and Dr. Hutton among them, taught that 'rivers have in general hollowed out their valleys'. This is no doubt true of rivulets and torrents . . . but the principal valleys in almost every great hydrographical basin in the world, are of a shape and magnitude which imply that they have been due to other causes besides the mere excavating power of rivers.

And

Professor Ramsay, and some other able geologists . . . incline, nevertheless, to the opinion that the great escarpments of the chalk may have been due to pluvial and fluviatile erosion, the sea, when it last retired, having left the secondary strata planed off at one and the same level. But this hypothesis seems to me untenable.

Fortunately W. Whitaker was able two years later (1867), to publish by permission the following clear statement by Lyell of a change of mind:

I have for long modified my opinion on denudation, and I now agree with you in considering that the escarpments round the Weald are not inland [sea] cliffs, as I formerly supposed, although at some points the sea may have entered through transverse valleys and modified parts of them. Two arguments, namely the fact of the escarpment of the Lower Greensand being parallel to that of the Chalk, and the fact that the sea cuts its cliffs successively through different formations and never keeps for such great distances to one formation only, are I believe unanswerable.

Fig. 20 The Grand Canyon, drawn by W. H. Holmes

We have already noted Lyell's deductions from earth pillars published in 1868.

The renaissance set in motion in Britain by Jukes was soon eclipsed by results of scientific exploration of the semi-arid regions of the American West dating from the foundation of the Geological Survey, U.S.A. We cannot enter into detail here, but merely recall the intrepid voyage of Major John Wesley Powell down the Grand Canyon—when the only casualties were three faint of heart who climbed out on the way and were killed by Indians—and the superb drawings of William Henry Holmes. These latter educated an immense audience as to the origin of scenery (Fig. 20).

In regard to Ramsay's theory of the glacial scooping out of rock-basins, presented at the Geological Society in 1862, Lyell apparently remained unconvinced to the end. Ramsay in 1862 happened to be President, just as Buckland had been in 1840; otherwise he used to say his paper would have been published only in bare abstract—for the older men on the Council were extremely hostile. It is difficult to assess opinion at the present day. Probably almost everyone attributes a host of minor rock-basins to glacial erosion, whereas a majority may think that most of the larger lakes of glaciated regions are due to earth-movement.

1863 *The Antiquity of Man*

Among Lyell's achievement of his latter years the *Antiquity of Man*, 1863, surely ranks highest. If it stood alone it would place him among the foremost of scientific authors. Its scope is amazing.

Chapter 1 discusses the geological time-significance of the terms Recent and Post-Pliocene, the latter presently to be replaced by Pleistocene. Lyell as a rule passed

Plate 23   Archaeopteryx—a reconstruction.

Plate 24   The Lyell Medal, founded in 1875.   (*Above*) obverse,
the head of Charles Lyell.   (*Below*) reverse, the three columns
of the Temple of Jupiter Serapis at Pozzuoli.

chronologically backwards in his survey of any geological subject.

Chapters 2 and 3 deal with Recent times and are of such geographical range as to include Danish peat mosses and kitchen middens, Swiss and Irish lake dwellings, certain American finds, and prehistoric canoes and whales unearthed in Scotland.

Chapters 4 and 5 pass back to the Post-Pliocene. They treat of human remains where the 'accompanying mammalia are extinct or belong to species not known to have lived within the times of history or tradition'. Lyell discusses with acceptance discoveries of such ancient man in southern France, at Liége in Belgium, and at Neanderthal, seventy miles northeast of Liége. He quotes a long description by Huxley of two skulls, one from Liége, the other from Neanderthal. They were very different. Lyell's cautious comment is

The direct bearing of the ape-like character of the Neanderthal skull on Lamarck's doctrine of progressive development and transmutation, or on that modification of it which has of late been so ably advocated by Mr. Darwin, consists in this, that the newly observed deviation from a normal standard of human structure is not in a casual or random direction, but just what might have been anticipated if the laws of variation were just such as the transmutationists require.

Chapters 6 to 11 are devoted in large measure to flint implements found in many cave deposits and alluvia throughout Europe, with special emphasis on those of the Somme valley and southern England. Chapters 12 to 18 give a comprehensive account of glacial phenomena in Europe and North America, with in several cases undue reliance upon the part played by floating ice. Special mention may be made of descriptions devoted to East Anglia and the Parallel Roads of Glen Roy.

Chapter 19 furnishes a recapitulation of previous

o

chapters. Chapters 20 to 22 are devoted to theories of progression and transmutation in the living world. Lyell gives a sympathetic, albeit critical account of Lamarck's development theory with its 'twin branches', progression and transmutation. Most geologists, with Lyell long in opposition, had recognized progress but had refused to link it with transmutation. Lyell now stresses that he had very early attributed extinction of species to natural causes. Passing on, he gives a long analysis of Darwin's and Wallace's views invoking transmutation guided by natural selection; and at the end of Chapter 21 he frankly admits that Darwin and Hooker have disposed of his arguments favouring successive creations. In Chapter 22 the difficulties arising from missing links are treated very fully. In the first place, it is clear that intermediate varieties linking species are in many cases quite well known. 'Scarcely any two botanists, for example, can agree as to the number of roses, still less as to how many species of bramble we possess'. In the second place, there is the blatant imperfection of the geological record. It is interesting that the discovery of *Archaeopteryx* is welcomed as an encouragement to geologists as to what strange creatures may yet be found (see Pl. 23); but we are told not to regard this fossil as a previously missing link, for Owen 'has shown that it is unequivocally a bird, and that such of its characters as are abnormal are by no means strikingly reptilian'.

Chapter 23 supplies a welcome comparison between the origin and development of species. Chapter 24 poses the question 'whether man can be regarded as an exception to the rule if the doctrine of transmutation be embraced for the rest of the animal kingdom'. Conflicting views are cited, including one that claims for man a separate kingdom in zoological classification, as a creature with 'the abstract notion of good and evil, right and wrong, virtue and vice, . . . a belief in a world beyond ours, and in certain mysterious beings, . . . in other words, the religious faculty'. Lyell leaves his readers to draw their own conclusions. This was a habit of which he often boasted.

Darwin in the somewhat querulous letter to Hooker, from which we have already quoted, says: 'The whole certainly struck me as a compilation, but of the highest quality, for when possible the facts have been verified on the spot, making it almost an original work. The Glacial chapters seem to me best, and in parts magnificent.' And so he continues, until, feeling perhaps that the word 'compilation' might be thought ungenerous, he adds between brackets '(You know I value and rank high compilers, being one myself!)'.

Darwin's mention of glaciation reminds us that Lyell never realized the lifting powers of glaciers. For him, all through, the sea-shells at 1,400 feet on Moel Tryfaen proved recent upheaval of the land to a corresponding extent.

1872-5 The Final Years

In April 1872 Lyell and his wife with the helpful company of T. McKenny Hughes went to the south of France, to the caves of Aurignac.

In a letter to Professor Heer dated 16 March 1873, Lyell concludes as follows:

You kindly wish me to tell you of my health, and that of Lady Lyell. As I am now half way through my seventy-fifth year, you will not be surprised to learn that my eyes, which have always been weak, from boyhood, are beginning to fail me, so that I am obliged to depend on other people for writing from dictation all my letters to correspondents, and for reading all the books which I study; but I am able to walk, enjoy life and society in moderation, and if you come to England when I am at home, I should be happy to show you hospitality. Your letters are always a great treat to me.

Then follows a bright insertion:

My dear Mr. Heer, I am perfectly well, thank you, and should be very glad to see you again. Very sincerely yours, Mary E. Lyell.

The next letter to Heer is dated 7 July 1873, and includes:

I have not written to you since the sudden and unexpected death on April 24 of my dear wife, with whom you were so well acquainted, and you can, I am sure, appreciate the shock which this has given me. I endeavour by daily work at my favourite science to forget as far as possible the dreadful change which this has made in my existence. At my age of nearly seventy-six the separation cannot be very long, but as she was twelve years younger, and youthful and vigorous for her age, I naturally never contemplated my surviving her, and could hardly believe it when the calamity happened. A feverish cold carried her off almost without pain or suffering.

I should be very glad to hear from you what chance I have of finding you in Zürich or the neighbourhood.

It will be a great pleasure to see an old friend whom I knew in happier days.

And so with McKenny Hughes, now Professor at Cambridge in succession to Sedgwick, and 'a sister' (?sister-in-law), who devoted herself to him for the rest of his days, he went abroad that autumn, and visited his friend Professor Heer of Zürich.

Here let us quote from Katherine Lyell, who edited the *Life and Letters* of her brother-in-law Charles.

In June 1874 he went to Cambridge, to receive the honorary degree of LL.D., and that same month was admitted to the freedom of the Turners' Company in the City of London. He spent some weeks in Forfarshire, and found pleasure in visiting some of his old haunts, and in finding that his theories of fifty years past still held good. [His interpretation of the local serpentine has since been considerably revised.] He invited Mr. Judd to join him, and went with him to several points of interest [and listened with pleasure to his story of Hebridean volcanoes].

On November 5, the fiftieth anniversary of the Geological Society Club, of which he had been a member from its foundation, he attended the dinner, and spoke with a vigour that surprised his friends.

His failing eyesight and other infirmities now began to increase rapidly, and towards the close of the year he became very feeble. But his spirit was ever alive to his old beloved science, and his affectionate interest and thought for those about him never failed. He dined downstairs on Christmas day with his brother's [Henry's] family, but shortly after that kept to his room.

His death took place on 22 February 1875. His brother who had been almost daily with him had been carried off a fortnight previously by a sudden illness. His friends, headed by Joseph Hooker, now President of the Royal Society, immediately petitioned that he should be buried in Westminster Abbey. Thither he was followed seven years later by his dearest friend, Charles Darwin.

Epilogue

It is appropriate to consider to what extent posterity is indebted to Lyell.

He did more than anyone else to free geology from the authority of tradition. He steadfastly sought truth through deduction from observation.

He, like a few predecessors, explained scenery by invoking earth-movement, erosion, and deposition acting with the same characters and the same intensities as prevail today. This is now universally accepted, though one must admit that Lyell for long weakened his case by underestimating the potency of subaerial erosion and relying too much on the waves of the sea.

He confirmed the importance of localized earth-movements in place of Werner's universal sea-movements. This holds, though sea-movements must not wholly be abandoned: for instance, the Glacial Period temporarily transferred an appreciable amount of oceanic water to the land.

His interest in earthquakes as geological phenomena is justified.

In the Alps, though not in Bohemia, he correctly assigned certain abnormal groupings of fossiliferous beds to earth-movement.

He usefully pointed out that changes in the distribution of land and sea may materially affect climate.

He early advocated that dispersal of erratics is largely

conducted by floating ice without associated torrents. True, he claimed too much for sea-ice as against land-ice, but he was one of the very first to apply, even on a limited scale, Agassiz's land-ice interpretation of the glaciation of Britain.

He successfully opposed the idea that mountain chains have been elevated suddenly, a view largely based on current misinterpretations of the origin of scenery and the dispersal of erratics.

He also exposed the absurdity of the idea that ordinary volcanoes are products of central upheaval with their craters produced by accompanying disruption rather than by explosion.

He played a great part in employing fossils to group the Tertiary formations into a convenient succession of systems.

He insisted as a matter of observation that change of faunas from formation to formation has often been accomplished piecemeal without the abrupt wholesale completeness claimed by typical catastrophists.

He ascribed extinction of species to natural causes, though until won over by Darwin he attributed origin of species to special creations.

He considered conjectures regarding the 'beginning' to lie outside the scope of geology.

In the many editions of his *Principles of Geology*, he consistently taught that all geological events, but not the origin of species, have been governed by laws of nature which are open to investigation at the present day. He thus prepared the way for Darwin's explanation of the origin of species by natural selection, though he himself accepted this extension of his thesis with very great reluctance.

His descriptions of geological phenomena in widely separated regions are to a wonderful degree based on personal investigation coupled with much reading and conversation. They are attractive and valuable to the present day.

His enlightened synthesis of geology with archaeology and anthropology has supplied enduring inspiration. His capacity for revising early, strongly held opinions is altogether admirable. It is nowhere better illustrated than in his *Antiquity of Man* which appeared in his sixty-sixth year.

Index